About the Authors

Dr. Mary Velasquez is Centennial Professor in Leadership for Community, Corporate, and Professional Excellence and director of the Health Behavior Research and Training Program at the University of Texas at Austin. Her research focuses on the development and testing of behavioral interventions in healthcare settings, screening and brief interventions, group treatment for substance use, and preventing fetal alcohol spectrum disorder.

Dr. Karen Ingersoll is associate professor of Psychiatry and Neurobehavioral Sciences at the University of Virginia School of Medicine, Charlottesville, VA. Dr. Ingersoll's focus is the intersection of addiction and health. She has developed and tested motivational interventions that target health behaviors and addictive behaviors together for two decades, including multiple studies of interventions to reduce the risk of alcohol-exposed pregnancy.

Drs. Linda and Mark Sobell are both professors at Nova Southeastern University, Ft. Lauderdale, FL, and have had a clinical research career spanning four decades. They are nationally and internationally known for their research in the addictions field, including the development of the Timeline Followback and Guided Self-Change model of treatment. They both have received several awards including the Jellinek Memorial Award for outstanding contributions to knowledge in the field of alcohol studies.

Advances in Psychotherapy – Evidence-Based Practice

Series Editor
Danny Wedding, PhD, MPH, School of Medicine, American University of Antigua, St. Georges, Antigua

Associate Editors
Larry Beutler, PhD, Professor, Palo Alto University / Pacific Graduate School of Psychology, Palo Alto, CA
Kenneth E. Freedland, PhD, Professor of Psychiatry and Psychology, Washington University School of Medicine, St. Louis, MO
Linda C. Sobell, PhD, ABPP, Professor, Center for Psychological Studies, Nova Southeastern University, Ft. Lauderdale, FL
David A. Wolfe, PhD, RBC Chair in Children's Mental Health, Centre for Addiction and Mental Health, University of Toronto, ON

The basic objective of this series is to provide therapists with practical, evidence-based treatment guidance for the most common disorders seen in clinical practice – and to do so in a reader-friendly manner. Each book in the series is both a compact "how-to" reference on a particular disorder for use by professional clinicians in their daily work and an ideal educational resource for students as well as for practice-oriented continuing education.

The most important feature of the books is that they are practical and easy to use: All are structured similarly and all provide a compact and easy-to-follow guide to all aspects that are relevant in real-life practice. Tables, boxed clinical "pearls," marginal notes, and summary boxes assist orientation, while checklists provide tools for use in daily practice.

Women and Drinking

Preventing Alcohol-Exposed Pregnancies

Mary Marden Velasquez
Health Behavior Research and Training Institute, University of Texas at Austin, TX

Karen S. Ingersoll
University of Virginia School of Medicine, Charlottesville, VA

Mark B. Sobell and Linda Carter Sobell
Center for Psychological Studies, Nova Southeastern University, Fort Lauderdale, FL

Library of Congress Cataloging in Publication information for the print version of this book is available via the Library of Congress Marc Database under the Library of Congress Control Number 2015930446

Library and Archives Canada Cataloguing in Publication

Velasquez, Mary Marden, author
 Women and drinking : preventing alcohol-exposed pregnancies / Mary Marden Velasquez (Health Behavior Research and Training Institute, University of Texas at Austin, TX), Karen S. Ingersoll (University of Virginia School of Medicine, Charlottesville, VA), Mark B. Sobell and Linda Carter Sobell (Center for Psychological Studies, Nova Southeastern University, Fort Lauderdale, FL).

(Advances in psychotherapy--evidence-based practice ; v. 34)

Includes bibliographical references.

Summary: "This book is written to help psychologists and other health care providers dentify and make referrals for women who might be at risk of an alcohol-exposed pregnancy (AEP), and to describe evidence-based interventions that are designed to prevent AEPs."--Preface.

Issued in print and electronic formats.

ISBN 978-0-88937-401-0 (paperback).--ISBN 978-1-61676-401-2 (pdf).--ISBN 978-1-61334-401-9 (html)

 1. Fetal alcohol syndrome--Prevention. 2. Women--Alcohol use--Prevention. 3. Pregnant women--Alcohol use--Prevention. I. Sobell, Linda C., author II. Sobell, Mark B., author III. Ingersoll, Karen S., author IV. Title. V. Series: Advances in psychotherapy--evidence-based practice ; v. 34

RG629.F45V44 2015   618.3'26861   C2015-901468-9
                                                 C2015-901469-7

Cover image © dardespot – istockphoto.com

© 2016 by Hogrefe Publishing
http://www.hogrefe.com

PUBLISHING OFFICES

USA: Hogrefe Publishing Corporation, 38 Chauncy Street, Suite 1002, Boston, MA 02111
          Phone (866) 823-4726, Fax (617) 354-6875; E-mail customerservice@hogrefe.com
EUROPE: Hogrefe Publishing GmbH, Merkelstr. 3, 37085 Göttingen, Germany
          Phone +49 551 99950-0, Fax +49 551 99950-111; E-mail publishing@hogrefe.com

SALES & DISTRIBUTION

USA: Hogrefe Publishing, Customer Services Department,
          30 Amberwood Parkway, Ashland, OH 44805
          Phone (800) 228-3749, Fax (419) 281-6883; E-mail customerservice@hogrefe.com
UK: Hogrefe Publishing, c/o Marston Book Services Ltd., 160 Eastern Ave.,
          Milton Park, Abingdon, OX14 4SB, UK
          Phone +44 1235 465577, Fax +44 1235 465556; E-mail direct.orders@marston.co.uk
EUROPE: Hogrefe Publishing, Merkelstr. 3, 37085 Göttingen, Germany
          Phone +49 551 99950-0, Fax +49 551 99950-111; E-mail publishing@hogrefe.com

OTHER OFFICES

CANADA: Hogrefe Publishing, 660 Eglinton Ave. East, Suite 119-514, Toronto, Ontario, M4G 2K2
SWITZERLAND: Hogrefe Publishing, Länggass-Strasse 76, CH-3000 Bern 9

Hogrefe Publishing
Incorporated and registered in the Commonwealth of Massachusetts, USA, and in Göttingen, Lower Saxony, Germany

Printed and bound in the USA

ISBN 978-0-88937-401-0 (print) • ISBN 978-1-61676-401-2 (PDF) • ISBN 978-1-61334-401-9 (EPUB)
http://doi.org/10.1027/00401-000

Preface

This book is written to help psychologists and other health care providers identify and make referrals for women who might be at risk of an alcohol-exposed pregnancy (AEP), and to describe evidence-based interventions that are designed to prevent AEPs.

The harmful effects of a women's drinking on her unborn child are not a new concern. Historically, while concerns about maternal drinking date back to biblical times, scientific investigations into fetal alcohol exposure were largely nonexistent through the early 1970s. In 1996, an Institute of Medicine (IOM) committee was charged with improving the understanding of available research knowledge and experience on approaches for diagnosing fetal alcohol syndrome (FAS) and related disorders as well as the prevalence of FAS and related disorders in the general population (Institute of Medicine, 1996). It was not until the IOM published its pivotal paper discussing issues related to the prevalence, diagnosis, treatment, and prevention of FAS, that we started to learn the extent of the full spectrum of fetal alcohol spectrum disorder (FASD). For example, we learned that fetal alcohol exposure was the leading known cause of intellectual disability in the Western world and, importantly, that FASD is a 100% preventable disability.

We also learned that drinking during pregnancy can cause birth defects; mild to severe intellectual disabilities; mental health problems; and emotional, learning, and behavioral problems called FASD (O'Connor & Paley, 2009; Streissguth et al., 2004). The most severe of these disorders, FAS, is associated with a combination of abnormal facial features, neurodevelopmental disorders, growth deficits, and overall poor outcomes. FASDs, including FAS, are a significant challenge for the scientific community and the health care system (Bertrand et al., 2004). Alcohol consumption among pregnant women is a significant public health concern, and preventing AEPs has been identified as a health care priority by several major and influential groups. Recommendations against drinking during pregnancy have been published by the IOM (Stratton, Howe, & Battaglia, 1996), the US Surgeon General's Office (Office of the Surgeon General, 2005), and the US Department of Health and Human Services, Office of Disease Prevention and Health Promotion (2011).

Although the best time to prevent AEPs is prior to conception, women – including those who intend to become pregnant – may not be aware that they have conceived until several weeks or months into their pregnancy. Consequently, during this key phase of fetal development, many women continue to drink. Further, half of all women of childbearing age drink alcohol, and nearly half of all pregnancies are unplanned. What we know today, and what is the focus of this book, is that a variety of brief motivational behavioral interventions developed for nonpregnant women of childbearing age can effectively prevent AEPs (Cannon et al., 2014). Health care practitioners from multiple disciplines (e.g., psychologists, physicians, social workers) are well suited to deliver these interventions because they are trained to target specific behavioral change, and because women of childbearing age present to a wide variety of practitioners in different health care settings. The multiple evidence-based Changing High-Risk Alcohol Use and Improving Contraception Effectiveness Study (CHOICES) and CHOICES-like interventions, which are described in Chapter 3, all have been shown to reduce the risk of AEP across multiple practice settings, ranging from those where risk is high (e.g., jails, mental health and substance abuse treatment centers), to more "opportunistic" settings that serve significant numbers of women of childbearing age (e.g., primary care clinics, universities and colleges), to brochures that can be provided at no cost in the community (e.g., health care settings, pharmacies, physicians' offices).

The work described in this book is based on clinical trials from several FASD prevention studies that were funded by the US Centers for Disease Control and Prevention (CDC) to reduce the incidence of AEP. These multisite research and dissemination efforts started with a program of research known as Project CHOICES, which had several objectives. The first was to identify community settings where women would be at a high risk for an AEP (Project CHOICES Research Group, 2002). The second objective was to develop, test, and refine a comprehensive behavioral program to reach women who were at risk of an AEP (Project CHOICES Intervention Research Group, 2003). An initial multisite randomized controlled trial (RCT), conducted from 2002 to 2005, demonstrated that the CHOICES intervention could reduce risks for an AEP, preventing the harmful effects of FAS and FASD (Floyd et al., 2007). The CHOICES efficacy study was awarded the 2008 Charles C. Shepard Science Award at the CDC for excellence in prevention and control.

The multisite CHOICES team consisted of several principal investigators including the four authors of this book along with Drs. R. Louise Floyd, Patricia Dolan Mullen, Mary Nettleman, Kirk von Sternberg, and Kenneth Johnson. Following the initial studies, and over the course of 15 years, several of the investigators have conducted a series of additional RCTs, with each successive study informing the next. These studies and their results are described in Chapter 3. The successful outcomes for the six CHOICES and the CHOICES-like studies are shown individually in the first six tables in Chapter 3. To better reflect the overall impact of the success of the six CHOICES and CHOICES like studies, a final table in Chapter 3 lists the percentage of women in the six studies who met criteria for an overall reduced risk of an AEP at 6 months postintervention for the CHOICES (experimental group) compared with a Standard FASD intervention group (control). Remembering that *all* women in this table, control or experimental, were at risk when they entered the studies, the percentages for reduced risk for a postintervention AEP even for the control groups are impressive. However, the percentage of change is higher in the CHOICES or CHOICES-like studies. These research studies were all conducted in very different settings (e.g., primary care, university-hospital based obstetrical/gynecology practices, urban jails, substance abuse treatment settings, Native American tribal settings, primary care medical settings, media-recruited samples), and they included both college students and nonstudent groups.

We "Four Musketeers" (as we have come to call ourselves over the years) encourage you to use the information and intervention strategies presented in this book in ways that best suit your practice and setting. Whether or not this intervention fits within your particular program or treatment context, we urge you to increase your knowledge about AEP prevention and to share this knowledge with your colleagues who may be unaware of the effects of alcohol on pregnancy. The impact of preventing just one pregnancy affected by alcohol is significant – preventing just one child from the effects of FAS could mean saving more than US $2 million across a person's lifetime, as well as avoiding the challenges that the children and their families face when dealing with FASD and the impact on the quality of their lives. We hope this book will be a valuable guide in helping you reduce the risk of AEP in the women you serve and in the communities in which you work.

Acknowledgments

We are indebted to our research teams and our families who supported us as we conducted the many years of research and writing that are reflected in this work. We want to thank Danny Wedding for his guidance (and patience) as we worked our way through a project that turned out to be much bigger and to take much longer than we originally anticipated.

The development of the CHOICES intervention was made possible by the invaluable contributions of the other Principal Investigators, Drs. Mary Nettleman, Pat Mullen, and Kenneth Johnson. We also greatly appreciate the assistance of Dr. Kirk von Sternberg, Dr. Nanette Stephens, Dr. Beth Pomeroy, Shannon Johnson, Kyle Pitzer, and Sophia Sarantakos who helped in the completion of this book. We thank Janet Sharkis and Leah Davies from the Texas Office for the Prevention of Developmental Disabilities for their unwavering support and advocacy in FASD prevention. Likewise, we appreciate the assistance of the staff members at the US Centers for Disease Control and Prevention (CDC) who provided us valuable assistance in the preparation of the book.

Finally, we offer our sincere thanks to our colleagues at the CDC's National Center on Birth Defects and Developmental Disabilities who guided many of the FASD prevention research and dissemination studies described in this book. Special thanks to R. Louise Floyd (to whom this book is dedicated) who captained the CHOICES program of research at the CDC, and to Colleen Boyle who oversaw and supported those efforts. These two individuals have believed in us, trusted us, advocated for us, and supported us – both scientifically and personally – through the challenges and successes of 20 plus years of collaboration in preventing alcohol-exposed pregnancies.

Finally, as we were in the final stages of finishing this book, we learned that the CDC, on September 12, 2014, announced that since being released in July of 2011, approximately 8,000 sets of the CHOICES curriculum package have been requested and distributed throughout the United States and other countries. This is a huge testament to the utility of the CHOICES intervention.

Dedication

We dedicate this book to Dr. R. Louise Floyd who recognized that preventing alcohol-exposed pregnancy required a new approach. We acknowledge her instrumental leadership in this area and her ongoing commitment to preventing fetal alcohol spectrum disorders.

Mary Velasquez
Karen Ingersoll
Mark Sobell
Linda Sobell

Table of Contents

1

Description

Although the harmful effects of drinking alcohol during pregnancy have been observed for centuries, only in the past few decades has the relationship between prenatal alcohol use and birth defects been demonstrated (Randall, 2001). The concept of fetal alcohol spectrum disorders (FASDs) is relatively new, yet there have been differing opinions about how to label this continuum of disorders. In this chapter, the history of FASD and diagnostic issues are discussed. In addition, the magnitude of the problem and its consequences for individuals, families, and society is presented. Although the book's focus is on the prevention of alcohol-exposed pregnancies (AEPs), this chapter will help practitioners better understand the concept of FASD, the individuals affected, and the types of preventive services available for such individuals.

1.1   What Are Fetal Alcohol Spectrum Disorders?

The term *fetal alcohol spectrum disorders* is not a clinical diagnosis; rather, it is an umbrella term that has been used to describe a range of effects in children whose mothers have consumed alcohol when pregnant (Riley, Infante, & Warren, 2011). This includes a range of physical, mental, behavioral, and/or learning disabilities related to alcohol exposure during gestation. The lifelong implications of FASD can include deficits in intellectual processes (e.g., problem solving, attention, learning, memory, visuospatial abilities, motor functioning, social skills). Often those diagnosed with FASD experience a number of mental health issues and have overall poor life functioning and negative outcomes (O'Connor & Paley, 2009; Streissguth et al., 2004). Fetal alcohol syndrome (FAS) is a condition that falls at the extreme end of the FASD continuum, and is associated with the most severe impairments in functioning.

FASD describes a range of effects in children related to maternal drinking during pregnancy

1.2   How Is FASD recognized?

Because our understanding of the effects of maternal drinking during pregnancy is evolving, the development of diagnostic criteria to identify FASD is relatively new. A diagnostic schema recognizing the physical effects (e.g., abnormal facial features, growth problems, central nervous system problems), which can be more directly observed and are characteristic of FAS, was first issued by the Institute of Medicine (IOM; Stratton, Howe & Battaglia, 1996).

While the current *International Classification of Diseases* (ICD-10; World Health Organization, 2011) recognizes FAS, it does not recognize FASD, which contains a wider range of significant neurodevelopmental and mental health symptoms often associated with prenatal alcohol exposure (Bertrand & Dang, 2012).

Clinical Pearl
FASD Is a SPECTRUM of Disorders

FAS is a condition that falls at the extreme end of the FASD continuum, and it is associated with the most severe impairments in functioning

Conventional understandings of the impact of drinking during pregnancy were based on conceptualizations of fetal alcohol syndrome (FAS), a condition that is often easily detected by hallmark facial abnormalities. Although FAS is the most severe diagnosis under the fetal alcohol spectrum disorder (FASD) umbrella, multiple and varied disabilities and symptoms can arise from prenatal exposure to alcohol, and we urge practitioners to avoid the conventional view based on FAS and recognize that FASD refers to a broad spectrum of disorders from mild to severe. To do otherwise will only perpetuate problems in screening and diagnosis. We encourage practitioners to develop a thorough understanding of the effects of AEP, and to modify their practices accordingly. For instance, many of the symptoms falling under the central nervous system dysfunction cluster (e.g., hyperactivity, impulsivity, attention deficits, learning and intellectual disabilities) are not accompanied by facial abnormalities, and cannot be physically measured like growth deficiencies. To provide needed services to the children and families affected by FASD, practitioners need to recognize the more subtle signs of FASD.

1.3   The History of FASD

Concerns about the dangers of drinking during pregnancy have a long history, dating back to the medical literature in the 1700s

The physical effects of drinking during pregnancy were noted dating back as far as the 1700s when the Royal College of Physicians of London reported that babies born to mothers who drank heavily during pregnancy were "weak, feeble, and distempered" (Royal College of Physicians of London, 1726, p. 253). A related concern was depicted in a 1751 lithograph, *Gin Lane,* which English artist William Hogarth produced during London's so-called gin epidemic. Hogarth's print, which includes an image of a drunken woman letting a child fall from her arms, is a social commentary about the rampant use of highly distilled alcohol at the time, especially among women. When Hogarth published his print, fetal and infant death rates were higher than in previous years, even though it was a period of good wages, plentiful food, and relative freedom from the epidemic diseases that typically accounted for high infant mortality (Warren & Bast, 1988).

Reports of alcohol's negative effects on children continued throughout the 18th and 19th centuries. The earliest description of what is meant by the term *fetal alcohol syndrome* came from Dr. William Sullivan, a deputy medical officer at a prison in England. Sullivan observed that pregnant women prisoners who were heavy drinkers not only had higher rates of miscarriages but also that the babies who survived often displayed distinctive patterns of birth defects (Sullivan, 1899). Dr. Sullivan also reported that mortality and stillborn rates for children born to alcoholic mothers were more than twice those of nonalcoholic mothers, and the more a woman drank during pregnancy, the greater the likelihood of fetal problems. During the anti-alcohol period of the 1920s and the onset of Prohibition in the United States, interest in FAS declined (Randall, 2001; Warren & Bast, 1988). Forty years later, in the early 1960s, interest in FAS gained some momentum with the publication of a few scientific articles. However, during this same period, many researchers tried to refute the idea that alcohol could be detrimental to an unborn baby (Warren & Bast, 1988).

Scientific interest in the effects of alcohol on birth outcomes and child development gained momentum in 1967 when a family physician, Alexandre LeMache, published a report in the French Academy of Medicine about his 37 years of work with more than 1,200 children born to alcoholic mothers (Warren & Bast, 1988). His observations included neurological and behavioral problems, mental retardation, genital malformations, facial anomalies, and a high infant death rate. Unfortunately, LeMache's report had a limited impact as it did not present diagnostic criteria that could have facilitated the identification of fetal alcohol effects (Hoyme et al., 2005). A subsequent French publication by Lemoine and his colleagues described anomalies in the children of parents with serious alcohol problems (Lemoine, Harousseau, Borteyni, & Menuet, 1968). This article also failed to receive much attention, perhaps because it was in French and because the journal had limited circulation. Several years later, a team of US researchers at the University of Washington, which included pediatric dysmorphologists and psychologists, reported patterns similar to those described by Lemoine.

In 1973, a landmark study published in *The Lancet* described a small group of children all born to mothers who drank heavily during pregnancy (Jones, Smith, Ulleland, & Streissguth, 1973). All of the children had similar facial characteristics, growth deficiencies, and central nervous system dysfunction. In another publication that same year, Jones and Smith (1973) were the first to use the term *fetal alcohol syndrome* (FAS), describing it as "a diagnosis for two" (i.e., the child and the mother). Following this, there was a flurry of research studies, mostly epidemiological in nature.

Jones and Smith (1973) were the first to use the term *fetal alcohol syndrome* (FAS), describing it as "a diagnosis for two"

From the 1970s on, epidemiological and case studies confirmed Jones and Smith's findings that maternal prenatal alcohol exposure can cause a pattern of permanent deficits in unborn children. By 1990, FAS had been documented in studies published in over 20 different languages (Abel, 1990). With sponsorship from the National Institute on Alcohol Abuse and Alcoholism (NIAAA), the first international meeting on FAS was held in Seattle, Washington, in 1980.

During the 1980s and 1990s, professionals and practitioners became increasingly aware of the problems caused by AEPs. As it became clear that a range of developmental problems were associated with maternal alcohol consumption, and that children with distinctive FAS facial features represented only the severe end of this spectrum, it was also clear that concern about maternal drinking during pregnancies should not be limited to those women who drink heavily (Calhoun, 2011). Shortly before his death, Smith made a plea for the field to recognize a wider spectrum of damage caused by prenatal drinking which he termed *fetal alcohol effects* (Smith, 1981). This term, which was later used to describe intellectual disabilities and behavioral problems resulting from an AEP, has today fallen out of favor. In 1981, the

US Surgeon General's Office first recommended warnings against alcohol use during pregnancy (Office of the Surgeon General, 1981), and in 1988, the US Congress passed legislation requiring that alcoholic beverages carry warnings stating that pregnant women should not drink alcohol. In 2005, this advisory was updated, warning women that the risk of a baby being born with any of the FAS conditions increases with the amount of alcohol a pregnant woman consumes, as does the severity of the condition (Office of the Surgeon General, 2005). The Surgeon General's advisory is shown in the text box.

Surgeon General's FAS Advisory of 2005

The discovery of FAS led to considerable public education and awareness initiatives informing women to limit the amount of alcohol they consume while pregnant. However, since that time, more has been learned about the effects of alcohol on a fetus. It is now clear that no amount of alcohol can be considered safe.

I now wish to emphasize to prospective parents, health care practitioners, and all childbearing-aged women, especially those who are pregnant, the importance of not drinking alcohol if a woman is pregnant or considering becoming pregnant.

Based on the current, best science available we now know the following:

Alcohol consumed during pregnancy increases the risk of alcohol-related birth defects, including growth deficiencies, facial abnormalities, central nervous system impairment, behavioral disorders, and impaired intellectual development. No amount of alcohol consumption can be considered safe during pregnancy. Alcohol can damage a fetus at any stage of pregnancy. Damage can occur in the earliest weeks of pregnancy, even before a woman knows that she is pregnant. The cognitive deficits and behavioral problems resulting from prenatal alcohol exposure are permanent. Alcohol-related birth defects are completely preventable.

For these reasons:
- A pregnant woman should not drink alcohol during pregnancy.
- A pregnant woman who has already consumed alcohol during her pregnancy should stop in order to minimize further risk.
- A woman who is considering becoming pregnant should abstain from alcohol.

Recognizing that nearly half of all births in the United States are unplanned, women of childbearing age should consult their physician and take steps to reduce the possibility of prenatal alcohol exposure.

Health professionals should inquire routinely about alcohol consumption by women of childbearing age, inform them of the risks of alcohol consumption during pregnancy, and advise them not to drink alcoholic beverages during pregnancy.

From Office of the Surgeon General, US Department of Health and Human Services (2005). Retrieved from http://www.cdc.gov/ncbddd/fasd/documents/surgeongenbookmark.pdf

---

1.4   Definitions of FASD and Related Disorders

"When a pregnant woman drinks alcohol, so does her baby" (Office of the Surgeon General, 2005, p. 1)

Over the years there have been several different terms used to describe what is now called FASD. For example, fetal effects of an AEP have been categorized as alcohol-related neurodevelopmental disorder (ARND) involving mental and behavioral impairments (e.g., learning disabilities, poor school performance, poor impulse control, problems with memory, attention, and/or judgment), or alcohol-related birth defects (ARBD) describing malformations of the skeletal system and major organ systems (e.g., defects of the heart, kidneys, bones, and/or auditory system). Other frequently used terms have been fetal alcohol effects (FAE; Smith, 1981) to describe the full range of disorders (Substance Abuse and Mental Health Services Administration [SAMHSA], 2009), and partial FAS (Institute of Medicine, 1996) for children who have some facial features of FAS and some growth retardation, neurodevelopmental problems, or behavior or cognitive abnormalities that cannot be explained by family background or environment alone.

Clinical Pearl
Commonly Used Terms

ARBD	Alcohol-related birth defects
ARND	Alcohol-related neurodevelopmental disorder
FAE	Fetal alcohol effects (term no longer used)
FAS	Fetal alcohol syndrome
FASD	Fetal alcohol spectrum disorder (Note: This is not a diagnostic term but an umbrella term that encompasses all disabilities caused by prenatal exposure to alcohol)
ND-PAE	Neurobehavioral disorder associated with prenatal alcohol exposure
pFAS	Partial fetal alcohol syndrome

In 2004, the National Organization on FASD (NOFAS) convened a task force to address the need to identify individuals with FASD and improve the delivery of services to individuals and their families. This group consisted of a broad range of experts (e.g., clinicians, researchers, parents, administrators) from several federal agencies (e.g., National Institutes of Health [NIH], CDC, SAMHSA). One of their major accomplishments was the development of specific guidelines for diagnosing FAS (Table 1).

1.5   Cause of FASD

The cause of FASD is clear: *any alcohol use during a woman's pregnancy*. If a woman does not drink alcohol when pregnant her baby cannot have FASD. When a woman does drink alcohol, the pattern and severity of problems caused by prenatal alcohol use depend on a number of factors including the timing, frequency, and quantity of alcohol exposure. It is still unclear why some women who drink alcohol when pregnant have babies with obvious damage, and others who drink similar amounts appear to have healthy babies with no discernible effects. Researchers are using animal models to investigate which factors (e.g., maternal nutrition, hormonal fluctuations) might alter the likelihood of alcohol exposure resulting in fetal damage (Caudill, 2010; Nguyen & Thomas, 2011). While some animal studies suggest that maternal nutritional deficiencies may contribute to the effects of alcohol during pregnancy, it does not necessarily follow that nutritional supplements would reduce the potential

There is no risk of a child suffering FASD if a woman does not drink when pregnant

for damage in humans. In the remainder of this chapter, the effects of alcohol on a developing fetus will be considered, followed by a discussion of the potential impact of this exposure across the lifespan.

1.6   How Does Alcohol Affect a Developing Fetus?

Risk of baby suffering an FAS condition increases with amount of alcohol a pregnant woman drinks, as does the risk for its severity

Alcohol can cause severe and permanent brain damage as early as third week of pregnancy when a developing embryo is only 0.5 mm in diameter

A *teratogen* is defined as any agent that can disrupt development of an embryo or fetus. Alcohol is a teratogen that crosses the placenta, and when a pregnant woman drinks, the alcohol consumed can affect the developing fetus. A woman's drinking during her pregnancy can have a profound impact on her unborn child at any time, particularly during the early weeks of gestation. Researchers have found that alcohol can cause severe and permanent brain damage as early as the third week of pregnancy when a developing embryo is only 0.5 mm in diameter, which is small enough to fit inside the zero on a penny (Collaborative Initiative on Fetal Alcohol Spectrum Disorders, 2012). The brain and central nervous system are also highly susceptible to the effects of prenatal alcohol. Some studies show that even light drinking during pregnancy can potentially place a child at risk for learning problems (e.g., slower reaction times, poor attention capabilities, lower intelligence; National Organization on Fetal Alcohol Syndrome [NOFAS] Colorado, 2013). Figure 1 shows alcohol exposure at different phases of embryo/fetal development and what part of the body it affects, with the darkest segments of each time line indicating the

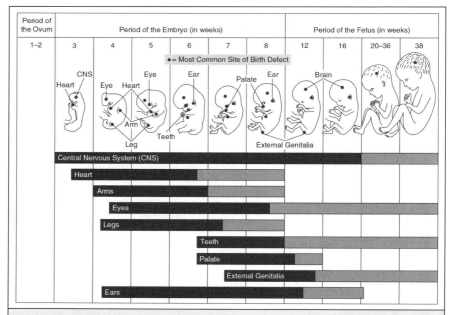

Figure 1
Alcohol exposure and phases of embryo/fetal development.
From National Institute on Alcohol Abuse and Alcoholism (2005). © NIAAA.

greatest sensitivity to alcohol. The lighter segments indicate periods of continued sensitivity to alcohol exposure during which physiological abnormalities and minor structural defects can still occur.

In some cases, FASDs (especially the disorders at the extreme end of the spectrum) are recognized at birth, especially when the mother's drinking history is known. In many cases, however, FASD is not identified until the child's problems become more apparent, and the negative effects of FASD are often first identified when a child experiences difficulties in school.

1.7   Effects of FASD Across the Lifespan

Individuals with FASD often grow up with social and emotional problems that cause them to encounter various difficulties as they move through the life cycle (e.g., mental illness, substance use disorders, difficulties in school or with the criminal justice system). As a person with FASD matures, the effects can be manifested in a variety of ways. The text box presents a list of characteristics often seen in people with FASD over different developmental periods.

Characteristics Often Seen in Individuals With FASD

Newborns or infants
- Sleep difficulties: unpredictable sleep/wake cycle
- Failure to thrive
- Feeding difficulties including weak sucking reflex
- Heart defects, kidney problems, or skeletal anomalies
- Easily overstimulated (increased sensitivity to light and sound)
- Neurological problems
- Poor fine motor control
- Poor gross motor control
- Seizures, tremors, or jitteriness
- Small size
- Susceptibility to infections

Preschoolers
- Small size
- Intellectual disabilities (mental retardation)
- Hyperactivity
- Lack of impulse control
- Emotional overreaction and tantrums
- Poor eye–hand and physical coordination
- Poor judgment (children are often overly friendly, being unable to recognize danger or have a healthy fear of strangers)
- Speech delays (slow vocabulary or grammar development, poor articulation, or perseverative speech)

Elementary school-aged children
- Poor impulse control
- Attention deficit disorders
- Hyperactivity
- Behavioral problems (acts such as lying, stealing, or defiance)

- Social difficulties (may include being overly friendly, immature, easily influenced by others, and difficulty with decision making)
- Language difficulties (delayed development, problems with expressive or receptive language)
- Learning disabilities or cognitive disabilities
- Memory difficulties
- Small size

Adolescents and young adults
- Low academic achievement
- Problems with abstract reasoning
- Poor judgment
- Difficulty in anticipating consequences
- Poor self-esteem
- Memory problems
- More pronounced impulsiveness (lying, stealing, or defiant acts)

Reprinted with permission from University of South Dakota, Sanford School of Medicine, Center for Disabilities. (2013). *Fetal alcohol spectrum disorders handbook* (p. 63). Sioux Falls, SD: Author. © 2013 University of South Dakota Sanford School of Medicine Center for Disabilities.
Original sources: CDC, 2014; FASCETS, 2010; National Organization on Fetal Alcohol Syndrome Colorado, 2013; Wattendorf & Muenke, 2005.

Because every individual is unique, not everyone will exhibit all of the characteristics related to FASD at any given age. When FASD is identified in infancy or early childhood, effective interventions can be put into place to help minimize negative consequences. Paley and O'Connor (2011) provide suggestions about effective behavioral strategies for working with children and adolescents with FASD. The US Substance Abuse and Mental Health Services Administration (SAMHSA) Treatment Improvement Protocol 58, titled *Addressing Fetal Alcohol Spectrum Disorders*, also provides information that can be used by practitioners to better identify patients in their practice who may have FASD. This publication also offers suggestions for referral, diagnosis, and intervention strategies for children, adolescents, and adults (SAMHSA, 2007).

1.8   Fetal Alcohol Syndrome

As mentioned earlier, FAS – the condition at the most extreme end of the FASD continuum – is the leading cause of intellectual disabilities in the United States. Diagnosing FAS can be difficult because there are no definitive tests (e.g., blood tests) or imaging technologies that can confirm a diagnosis. Over the years, the ability to diagnose FAS has been expanded and refined, but some controversy remains about which criteria to use. The various schemas all agree on the facial characteristics that characterize FAS, but they differ in how many other features or problems must be present for a definitive diagnosis. The most distinctive facial characteristics are (a) short palpebral fissures (i.e., the space between the margins of the eyelids), (b) a smooth philtrum (i.e., the vertical groove above the upper lip), and (c) a thin vermilion (i.e., the border of the upper lip). Details on each of the diagnostic schemas can be found in the literature (Astley & Clarren, 2000; Bertrand et al., 2004; Chudley et al., 2005; Hoyme et al., 2005). Despite some differences, the schemas all rely on anomalies in three distinct areas: (a) prenatal and/or postnatal growth deficiency, (b) central nervous system (CNS) dysfunction, and (c) characteristic pattern of facial anomalies (Riley et al., 2011). The facial features are the easiest to recognize in children between the ages of 3 and 14 years. As children with FAS grow older, the facial features may change, making FAS more difficult to recognize. Figure 2 shows a drawing of the primary facial characteristics used in the diagnosis of FAS. Table 1 lists the guidelines for diagnosing FAS. These guidelines are intended to provide standard diagnostic criteria for FAS (Bertrand et al., 2004).

Table 1
Guidelines for Diagnosing Fetal Alcohol Syndrome

Abnormal facial features	Three distinct facial features: • Smooth ridge between the nose and upper lip • Thin upper lip • Short distance between the inner and outer corners of the eyes; wide-spaced appearance	
Growth problems	Height and/or weight lower than normal (< 10th percentile)	
Central nervous system problems	Structural	Differences in structure of the brain: • Smaller-than-normal head size • Significant changes in the structure of the brain
	Neurological	Problems with the nervous system: • Poor coordination • Poor muscle control • Problems with sucking as a baby
	Functional	Functions below what's expected for his or her age, schooling, or circumstances: • Cognitive deficits (e.g., low IQ) or Problems in at least three of the following areas: • Cognitive deficits or developmental delays • Executive functioning deficits • Motor functioning delays • Attention problems or hyperactivity • Problems with social skills • Other problems such as sensitivity to taste or touch, difficulty reading facial expression, and difficulty responding appropriately to common parenting practices

Adapted from Bertrand et al. (2004).

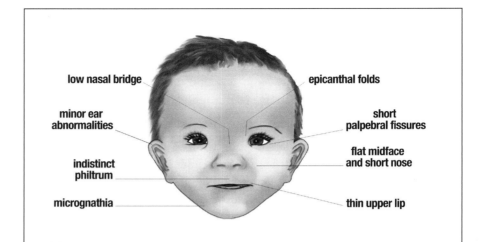

low nasal bridge

epicanthal folds

minor ear
abnormalities

short
palpebral fissures

flat midface
and short nose

indistinct
philtrum

micrognathia

thin upper lip

Figure 2
Fetal alcohol syndrome.
Reprinted with permision from Warren, K. R., Hewitt, B. G., & Thomas, J. D. (2010).
Fetal alcohol spectrum disorders: Research challenges and opportunities. *Alcohol
Research & Health: The Journal of the National Institute on Alcohol Abuse and
Alcoholism, 34*(1), 5. © 2010 by the National Institute on Alcohol Abuse and
Alcoholism.

1.9   Epidemiology of FASD and Related Disorders

1.9.1   How Prevalent Is FASD?

While there has been considerable progress over the last few decades in describing and identifying FASD, the prevalence of this disorder is still underestimated. Consequently, the full magnitude of the problem is unknown. Two other factors also contribute to the underestimation of FASD: (a) because most health care practitioners who work with children rarely screen for FASD, many children are not identified or counted in programs that monitor birth defects and developmental disabilities (Calhoun, 2011); and (b) there are wide variations in the identification of FASD, depending on the population sampled and the assessment method used. A review by May and colleagues (2009) estimated the prevalence of FASD in the United States to be at least 2 to 7 per 1,000 live births. However, in a more recent study using a middle class mainstream school population, May et al. (2014) found this estimate to be 24 to 48 per 1,000, substantially higher than general population estimates.

According to the CDC, of the approximately 4 million infants born each year in the United States, an estimated 1,000 to 6,000 will be born with FAS (CDC, 2004). The prevalence estimates for the entire FASD spectrum range are from 1% to 5%, with similar rates documented in other Western countries and even larger figures in countries with high rates of poverty (e.g., South Africa; Paley & O'Connor, 2011). Some children appear to be at even greater risk for FAS and FASD than others. For example, Native Americans in the United States have higher FAS rates compared with the US population in

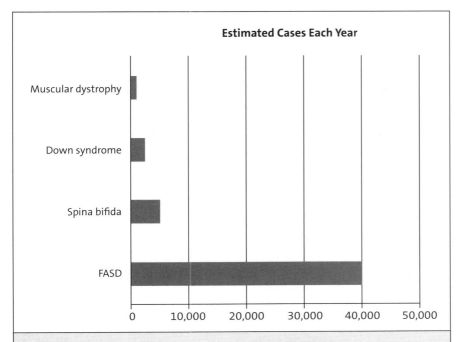

Figure 3
Estimates of fetal alcohol spectrum disorder (FASD) and other common childhood disabilities.
Reprinted with permission from National Organization on Fetal Alcohol Syndrome (NOFAS). (2014). *FASD: What everyone should know.* © 2014 by the National Organization on Fetal Alcohol Syndrome.

general. In a 2013 meta-analysis of 33 studies evaluating individuals across child-care systems (e.g., orphanages, foster care) in 12 countries, the pooled FAS prevalence and FASD prevalence rates were 6.0% and 16.9%, respectively (Lange, Shield, Rehm, & Popova, 2013). Figure 3 shows the number of estimated cases of FASD compared with other common developmental disabilities (e.g., Down syndrome, spina bifida).

Clinical Pearl
The Importance of FASD Prevention and Screening in High-Risk Community Settings

The prevalence of FASD appears to be higher in certain populations and particular settings. When conducting screening and prevention efforts with high-risk populations of women, we advise practitioners to remember that FASD addresses a spectrum of disorders from mild to severe. For example, FASD prevention efforts might especially benefit some Native American communities. Likewise, screening for FASD in foster care settings might bring help to children who require services. Finally, remember that women do not need to have an alcohol problem to be at risk of an AEP, as risky drinking relates to effects on an unborn child.

1.9.2   Costs of FASD

FASD is a major public health problem that affects individuals, families, and society (Riley et al., 2011). The emotional, physical, and social costs of this disability are lifelong and immense. No dollar amount can fully express the costs to individuals who are affected or their families. Families of individuals with FASD often are faced with (a) a scarcity of diagnostic and treatment services, (b) professionals who do not fully comprehend the nature of the disorder, and (c) lack of social support (Olson, Oti, Gelo, & Beck, 2009).

Individuals with FASD are known to be at greatly increased risk for a host of disabilities and problems with intellectual functioning and emotional regulation that may in turn contribute to many other difficulties (e.g., school failure, delinquency, substance use disorders; Alati et al., 2008; Streissguth et al., 2004). The text box, based on several scientific studies of individuals with FASD, shows the percentage of individuals with FASD who have other serious life problems.

Individuals With FASD Who Have Other Serious Life Problems

94% also have a mental illness

82% are unable to live independently

72% have experienced physical or sexual abuse, or domestic violence

60% have had disrupted school experiences

60% of those over the age of 12 have been charged with or convicted of a crime

45% have engaged in inappropriate sexual behavior

35% of adults and adolescents have been in prison for a crime

35% have alcohol and drug problems

Reprinted with permission from Texas Office for the Prevention of Developmental Disabilities. (2014). *Fetal alcohol spectrum disorder*, http://www.topdd.state.tx.us/fasd/. © 2014 Texas Office for the Prevention of Developmental Disabilities.
Source: Streissguth, A. P., Barr, H. M., Kogan, J., & Bookstein, F. I. (1996). *Final report to the Centers for Disease Control and Prevention (CDC)* (Tech. Rep. No. 96-06). Seattle, WA: Fetal Alcohol & Drug Unit.

FASD is a lifelong condition, and its related problems differ as individuals develop over their lifespan. Dollar estimates of the cost of FASD vary, depending on the source and how they are calculated. The National Organization on Fetal Alcohol Syndrome (2013) estimates the lifetime cost of treatment for one individual with FAS to be US $1.4 million. The majority of these costs are for medical and mental health treatment and special education. When considering the full range of FASD problems, the annual costs in the United States are estimated at US $3.6 billion. Research in other countries reflects similarly high costs related for FASD (Stade et al., 2009; Thanh & Jonsson, 2009).

Although the effects of FASD cannot be reversed, with early diagnosis and adequate treatment and service provision, they can be accommodated

While the effects of FASD cannot be reversed, with early diagnosis and adequate treatment and service provision, these effects can be accommodated. This means that individuals with FASD can grow, improve, and learn to function better throughout their lives. The best way to help prevent FASD, however, is by teaching others, particularly women of reproductive age, about the dangers of using alcohol during pregnancy. Appendices 1 and 2 provide links to useful websites for guides and resources that are currently available for free to practitioners. Advocating for the addition of evidence-based preconception care programs that will help prevent AEPs is an important national public health priority. Chapter 3 describes several of the programs that have successfully prevented AEPs.

2

Theories and Models of FASD

2.1   What Puts Women at Risk?

Two behaviors must occur simultaneously to put any woman at risk of an AEP: (a) drinking alcohol and (2) not contracepting effectively or not contracepting at all. When alcohol use and pregnancy occur together, the potential consequence is that women can have a child with an FASD. Therefore, when considering how to prevent an AEP and a possible FASD, the discussion must also include whether the woman is contracepting effectively. Nearly half of all pregnancies in the United States are unintended (i.e., mistimed, unplanned, or unwanted at the time of conception). This number for many years has remained unchanged (Henshaw, 1998). The CDC reported that in 2006, 49% of pregnancies were unintended – a slight increase from 48% in 2001 (CDC, 2013). They also indicated that the rate of unintended pregnancies is much higher for women aged 19 years and younger (i.e., more than three out of four pregnancies were unintended in that age group).

In this section, we will discuss factors that create a risk for an AEP, including women's drinking patterns, rates of alcohol metabolism, how effective contraception is defined, the estimates of the number of women who do not use contraception effectively, and the high incidence of unplanned pregnancies. We want to help readers understand the importance of two things: (a) promoting healthy, low-risk drinking among women of reproductive age and effective contraception until women decide to get pregnant, and (b) decreasing the risks of FASD.

2.1.1   What Is an Alcohol-Exposed Pregnancy?

Mengel and his colleagues (2006) provided a straightforward definition of an AEP: It is a pregnancy that occurs *any time a woman drinks any amount of alcohol and is pregnant, irrespective of whether she is aware of being pregnant.* Consumption of alcohol includes any type of alcoholic beverage (e.g., beer, hard liquor, regular or fortified wine, apéritifs) consumed in any amount. Consistent with this definition, a NIAAA fact sheet on FASD states: "Fetal alcohol exposure occurs when a woman drinks while pregnant. Alcohol can disrupt fetal development at any stage during a pregnancy – including before a woman knows she is pregnant" (NIAAA, 2013, para. 1). Specifically, alcohol can interfere with the development of an embryo/fetus in known ways, including brain damage, organ and tissue damage, and malformed facial features.

While the Mengel et al. and NIAAA definitions of an AEP capture every possible scenario of drinking during pregnancy, these definitions may not convey the type of drinking during pregnancy that is the *most likely* to result in problems. Although most women who are not planning to get pregnant cease drinking once they recognize they are pregnant, it is possible that even having a sip or a drink of alcohol before recognizing that they are pregnant will cause problems.

2.1.2   CDC Definition of an AEP

Women who are contracepting effectively and drinking are generally not going to be at risk of an AEP. However, the current CDC guidelines state that drinking ≥ 8 standard drinks (SDs; 1 SD = 14 g absolute ethanol per week and/or ≥ 4 SDs in a day (i.e., risk drinking) will put a woman at risk of an AEP if she is *not* contracepting or contracepting ineffectively. These drinking levels are consistent with those recommended by the NIAAA (NIAAA, 2004) for women's drinking in general.

2.1.3   Guidelines of Project CHOICES

When the project Changing High-Risk Alcohol Use and Improving Contraception Effectiveness Study (Project CHOICES) was conducted, the epidemiological data suggested using an AEP risk criterion of ≥ 5 SDs on at least 1 day (Jacobson & Jacobson, 1999). Several years later, the CDC adopted a slightly lower binge threshold level of ≥ 4 SDs in a day (Bertrand, Floyd, & Weber, 2005; Sayal et al., 2009). This is the definition used in the field today.

The Project CHOICES' perspective, consistent with a harm reduction approach (Marlatt & Witkiewitz, 2002), views an AEP as stemming from risky drinking at any time during pregnancy, but especially prior to when women learn they are pregnant. Because it is unlikely that all women of reproductive age will abstain from alcohol entirely on the chance that they might become pregnant, a harm reduction approach stresses counseling women to drink at a low risk level when they do drink in order to lessen the risk to the fetus should they unintentionally become pregnant. In the case of an unplanned or unintended pregnancy, a woman who has been drinking at a low risk level and who ceases drinking once she recognizes she is pregnant has probably reduced the risk of harm to her unborn child.

Although a recent series of papers on a Danish cohort of pregnant women found no evidence that light, occasional drinking causes harm, they did find that higher levels of consumption were associated with harm (Falgreen Erickson et al., 2012; Kesmodel, Bertrand, et al, 2012; Kesmodel, Falgreen Erickson, et al., 2012; Flak et al., 2014).

In summary, although the definition of low-risk drinking varies slightly regarding what amount puts women at risk of an AEP, experts and organizations warn women who may become pregnant to "abstain from alcohol consumption in order to eliminate the chance of giving birth to a baby with any of the harmful effects of the Fetal Alcohol Spectrum Disorders" (Office of the US Surgeon General, 2005, para. 1). Although this conservative and safe recommendation would avoid an AEP, *it is not practical to suggest that all women of reproductive age abstain from alcohol permanently on the chance that they might inadvertently become pregnant*, particularly when over half of all pregnancies are unplanned.

What is important to remember is that the above definition, used in Project CHOICES studies, allows women to make a *CHOICE* to not drink at all or to effectively use contraception and to consume alcohol at low risk levels. To better understand what is meant by *at risk of an AEP,* we will examine women's drinking in some depth.

> **The CHOICES intervention gives nonpregnant women a CHOICE to not drink at all or to contracept effectively and consume alcohol at low risk levels**

2.1.4   Women and Drinking

Alcohol's Impact Varies by Consumption

The impact of drinking alcohol for anyone can range from almost no observable effects to severe or life-threatening health problems, and death. Generally, irrespective of sex, greater drinking is associated with greater risk and more negative consequences. The IOM in 1990 issued a congressionally mandated report on alcohol treatment in the United States that showed that a large proportion of Americans are abstainers or drinkers who do not experience problems, with a decreasing proportion experiencing problems ranging from mild to severe (Institute of Medicine, 1990).

Figure 4 shows how drinking is distributed in the US population, and how it relates to drinking problem severity. As shown in this figure, most people are nondrinkers or light drinkers, with the majority of light drinkers having no or mild problems (e.g., occasional headaches from drinking). Two other

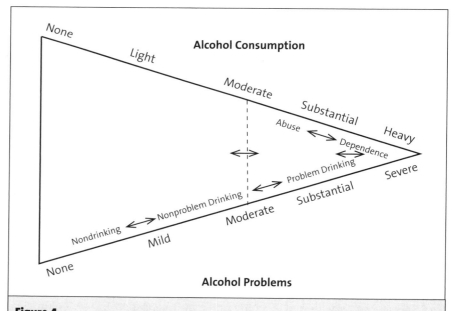

Figure 4
Distribution of alcohol consumption and alcohol problems in the US population.

things are noteworthy about this figure: (a) a small percentage of drinkers who drink a lot also experience severe alcohol-related problems; and (b) as drinkers move from moderate to heavier drinking, the likelihood of their experiencing alcohol problems increases, as does the severity of the problem.

Most of the harm caused by alcohol is not caused by those who fall into the small end of the triangle with the heaviest drinkers who have the most severe problems. On a population level, the middle group, whose drinking is moderate to substantial, causes the most harm (e.g., physical, psychological, social, legal) because of the large number of drinkers in this group (Kaner et al., 2009). Although such drinkers are less likely to suffer physical dependence on alcohol, cirrhosis, and other chronic health problems, compared with those in the small end of the triangle, their drinking does cause numerous and multiple problems associated with acute intoxication (e.g., drunk driving, interpersonal conflict, accidental injury).

Most of the harm caused by alcohol comes from drinkers who drink moderately

What Is Risky Drinking for Women?

Ten years ago, the NIAAA (2004) convened a panel of experts to develop definitions of recommended drinking, and what amount of alcohol constituted risk. This report, which defined drinking levels by sex, defined low-risk drinking for women as ≤ 3 SDs in a day, or ≤ 7 SDs per week (NIAAA, 2004). These guidelines are now part of the US Dietary Guidelines (US Department of Agriculture, 2010). In contrast, risky drinking is defined as ≥ 4 SDs in a day, or ≥ 8 SDs/week. These recommendations were derived from large epidemiological studies that have shown more harm to health, social, legal, occupational, and psychological status among those who consume more at risky levels, compared with those who drink at nonrisky levels (Bertrand, Floyd, & Weber, 2005; Sayal et al., 2009). For women, the recommendation to drink ≤ 3 SDs in a day is related to estimates based on women's metabolism and typical body weight, suggesting that consuming 3 drinks over a 2-hour period raises their blood alcohol concentration (BAC) to about 0.08% (which is the legal limit for "driving under the influence" [DUI] in all 50 states). There are also data that show physical harm is related to overall BAC over time. These criteria were selected from four sets of US drinking guidelines that had the best sensitivity and specificity, that incorporated both daily and weekly limits, and that did the best job of predicting several different alcohol-related outcomes (e.g., dependence, several health problems, impaired driving; Dawson, 2000).

What Is a Standard Drink?

The NIAAA definition of low-risk drinking uses a *standard drink* (SD) as the metric for estimating the amount of absolute alcohol consumed. While guidelines vary by country, they are intended to help practitioners and drinkers know the level of alcohol they are consuming. One SD in the United States contains 0.6 oz of absolute alcohol (14 g absolute ethanol). Thus, when comparing different alcoholic beverages in terms of beer, wine, and hard liquor, the following are all 1 SD: (a) a 12-oz (355-mL) glass or bottle of beer containing 5% alcohol by volume; (b) a 5-oz (148-mL) glass of regular wine containing 12% alcohol by volume; and (d) a 1.5-oz (44-mL) shot of 80-proof (40% by volume) hard liquor. The chart in Figure 5 illustrates how different alcoholic beverages equate to 1 SD. The alcohol equivalency can be derived

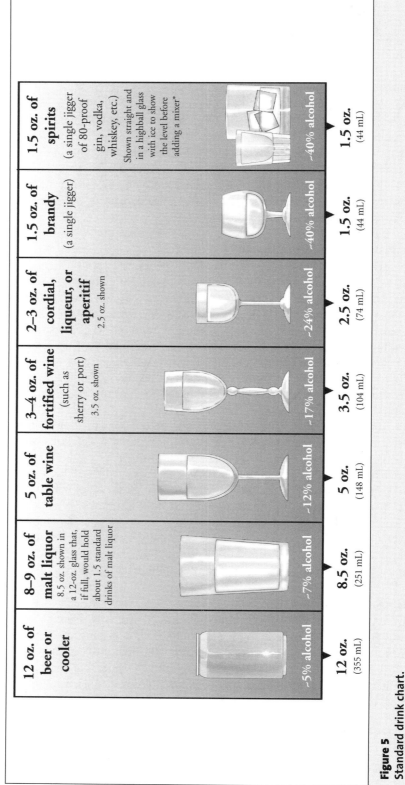

Figure 5
Standard drink chart.
Reprinted with permission from US Department of Health and Human Services. (2005). *Helping patients who drink too much: A clinicians guide* (updated 5th ed., p. 24). © 2005 by the National Institute on Alcohol Abuse and Alcoholism (NIAAA).

by multiplying the number of ounces by the percentage alcohol per volume: (a) beer: 12 oz (355 mL) x 5% = 60% alcohol by volume; (b) regular wine: 5 oz (148 mL) x 12% = 60% alcohol by volume; and (c) hard liquor: 1.5 oz (44 mL) x 40% = 60% alcohol by volume.

Epidemiology of US Women's Drinking

The Maternal and Child Health Bureau conducts a National Health Interview Survey in the United States that asks about drinking and other health issues among the general population. The most recent survey shows that in 2012, 39.6% of women aged 18 and older report drinking at least one alcoholic drink in the past year (US Department of Health and Human Services, 2013). Of those women who drank in the past year, when they did drink, they consumed a mean 2 SDs per day. Half of the women (50.8%) who drank were classified based on their self-reports as light drinkers ($\leq$ 3 SDs per week), 28.1% as infrequent drinkers (1–11 total SDs per year), 13.4% as moderate drinkers (3–7 SDs per week), and 7.7% as heavy drinkers ($\geq$ 8 SDs per week).

Binge drinking, defined as drinking $\geq$ 4 SDs in a single day in the past month, was reported by 16.8% of women, and heavy drinking, defined as drinking more than 1 SD on average per day in the past month was reported by 7.3% of women. Binge and heavy drinking varies by age (US Department of Health and Human Services, 2013). One third of young women (33%) between the ages of 18 to 25 reported binge and heavy drinking in the past month, compared with 11.5% of women in other age groups. Binge drinking was also more common than heavy drinking among all races and ethnic groups. Rates of past month binge drinking ranged from a high of 27.7% among Native Hawaiian/Pacific Islanders to a low of 7.9% for Asian women. Lastly, women reported on average 3.2 episodes of binge drinking per month, and when engaging in binge drinking, they averaged 5.9 drinks per day.

The Behavioral Risk Factors Survey Study interviewed women ages 18–44, which is considered the peak period of fertility (CDC, 2012). Of the 345,076 women interviewed, only 4% (n = 13,880) were pregnant. In the past 30 days, the percentage of nonpregnant and pregnant women who drank any alcohol or engaged in binge drinking was 51.5% and 15.0%, and 7.6% and 1.4%, respectively. It is troubling that for both pregnant and nonpregnant women who reported binge drinking in the last 30 days, the estimated average frequency and intensity of binge drinking were similar, about three times per month and six drinks per occasion.

Contraceptive Practices

There are two ways to prevent an AEP. We have just discussed one of these – drinking alcohol at low risk levels. The second way is to use contraception effectively. Unfortunately, while many women report using birth control methods, the effectiveness of different methods varies (Trussell, 2011). Further, many women have little or no knowledge about what constitutes effective contraception (Moos, Bartholomew, & Lohr, 2003; Pratt, Stephenson, & Mann, 2014). Consequently, if we want to prevent an unwanted pregnancy and an AEP, women must be advised about, and use, effective methods of contraception.

> **Clinical Pearl**
> **Addressing Contraception With Patients**
>
> Because many women are not aware of the many contraceptive options available to them, practitioners need to inquire about their patients' current and past methods of contraception. Even if there are more efficacious options, some women stay with the same method they started with, because of fear, misunderstanding, and comfort with the familiar. Costs and access to methods vary widely across states, so clinicians should become familiar with those in their local area. Practitioners who do not have prescriptive privileges can either recommend the woman go to her obstetrician/gynecologist (OB/GYN) or give her referrals to local family planning clinics (Note: For local family planning clinics search the Web using the words *family planning clinics* and insert local city name).

Unintended Pregnancy

An unintended pregnancy is one that was not planned or wanted at the time of the conception, either due to pregnancy occurring at the wrong time or being unwanted. Unintended pregnancies can be reduced dramatically with the use of effective contraception. Despite this, from 2006 to 2010, over 10% of women of reproductive age who were not sterile and were not trying to get pregnant had intercourse and reported no use of contraception (Mosher, Jones, & Abma, 2012). In the United States, this means that 4.7 million women per year are at risk of an unintended pregnancy. Recent studies estimate that the rate of women who used no birth control methods during the last time they had sexual intercourse was between 11% and 44% (Rahman, Berenson, & Herrera, 2013).

2.2   Who Is at Risk for an AEP?

A few epidemiological surveys have been specifically designed to determine the rate of women at risk for an AEP. In the first, 2,672 women who spoke English and were of reproductive age (i.e., 18–44 years) were recruited from different sites (i.e., urban jail, media-recruited sample, two primary care clinics, drug/alcohol treatment facility, urban gynecology clinic) in three different states. These women were surveyed about their drinking and use of contraceptive methods (Project CHOICES Research Group, 2002). Of the full sample, 12.5% of the women (n =333) were at risk for an AEP. Factors that were related to an AEP risk included recent drug use, which tripled the odds of AEP risk, and a history of smoking, which nearly doubled it. In addition, inpatient treatment for addiction or mental health problems, being arrested, reporting multiple sexual partners, and experiencing recent physical abuse all significantly increased the odds of an AEP. These findings suggest that screening for some groups of women with certain experiences related to an increased risk of an AEP is essential.

Clinical Pearl
Screening for AEP Risk

Because screening for an AEP includes both at-risk drinking and at-risk contraceptive use (i.e., ineffective or no contraception), we recommend that practitioners routinely screen their patients for both behaviors. We recommend that you routinely ask all female patients of reproductive age, *"Are you planning or hoping to become pregnant in the next year?"* If the woman responds with yes, ask her the single binge drinking question (see Section 2.3.1) regarding her drinking over the past 90 days. If she responds with no, you can also ask about her methods of contraception and give her a referral if necessary to a local family planning clinic. For women who affirmatively answer the single binge question, practitioners may want to further evaluate their patient's risky drinking in terms of whether she would benefit from further screening and perhaps a brief intervention for her alcohol use.

A second study examined the risk of an AEP among university women aged 18 to 24 years of age (Ingersoll, Ceperich, Nettleman, & Johnson, 2008). The survey was completed anonymously and voluntarily by 2,012 women recruited at student health clinic appointments, at recruitment booths on campus, and by phone calls in response to ads for a health education study. The majority ($n = 1,296$, 64%) reported drinking at risky levels in the past 90 days (i.e., binge drinking ≥ 5 SDs in a single day or drinking a mean ≥ 8 SDs per week). Although nearly all sexually active women used some form of contraception (94%), 18% of those used their method ineffectively, and thus were at risk for an unplanned pregnancy. Sexually active women had higher rates of risk-level drinking than their nonsexually active peers did. Given that most of the sexually active young women used some form of contraception, their risky drinking may be related to believing they would not become pregnant. The authors also found that at-risk drinking increased the odds of ineffective contraception by 1.7 times, suggesting that when engaging in risky drinking, women, particularly young women, forgot to use or wrongly used their method of contraception, and this, coupled with an inclination for younger people to engage in risk taking and experimentation, led to increased risk of an AEP (Winograd & Sher, 2015). Lastly, these results, which are consistent with past epidemiological studies of college drinking, suggest that all young women in college who drink at risk levels should be screened for risk of an AEP.

A study in Russia evaluated the risk of an AEP among women at two obstetrics and gynecology (OB/GYN) clinics. The definition of risk drinking for an AEP was the same as that currently used in the United States. In comparison to US studies, this study found exceptionally high rates of risk for an AEP in Russian women in both urban (54%) and rural (32%) areas, with no difference in alcohol consumption among women who might become pregnant and their peers not planning to become pregnant (Balachova et al., 2013). This finding was not surprising, as nearly all Russian women report drinking in the year before becoming pregnant.

Taken together, these three specifically focused epidemiological surveys indicate that many women are at risk for an AEP. Together, they support the need for systematic national and international screening of women who might be at risk for an AEP. Routinely screening women at risk of an AEP and simply providing them information so they can make better-informed decisions about their alcohol use and methods of contraception is a superb population-level approach for preventing AEPs.

2.3   Screening for At-Risk Drinking

When screening women for being at risk of an AEP, the evaluation would involve risky drinking, whether women are using birth control methods, and whether their methods are effective. There are several effective screening methods and measures that can be used for risky drinking related to an AEP. Although one single question related to binge drinking is recommended for use when screening due to the limited time health care providers have with patients, a few other measures will be discussed for practitioners that require additional information about women's use of alcohol.

2.3.1   Single Binge Drinking Question

The NIAAA has recommended that a single binge drinking (SBD) question be used to screen people who drink at risky levels. In a study that screened 286 primary care patients, an SBD question correctly identified 81.8% of those with "unhealthy" alcohol use, defined as the presence of an alcohol use disorder or risky consumption (Smith, Schmidt, Allensworth-Davies, & Saitz, 2009). Other studies of problem drinkers have found similar results using an SBD question (Cyr & Wartman, 1990; Stewart, Borg, & Miller, 2010; Taj, Devera-Sales, & Vinson, 1998).

Two recent studies that have targeted women who were at risk of an AEP have also used an SBD question. Both studies, one in the United States ($N = 354$; Johnson, Sobell, & Sobell, 2010), and one in Russia ($N = 689$; Balachova et al., in press) involved large numbers of women of reproductive age with a known risk for an AEP. Both studies at the end of their trials evaluated how many of the originally selected study participants would have been correctly identified as being at risk of an AEP using the SBD question: "How often did you have four or more drinks on one occasion?" (Note: When the US study was conducted, the epidemiological data suggested using an AEP risk criterion of ≥ 5 SDs in a day.) In both the Russian and US study, almost all women who were at risk of an AEP in the 90 days prior to the study were correctly identified by the SBD question – that is, 99% and 98%, respectively.

2.3.2   Weekly Drinking ≥ 8 SDs as a Risk Factor for AEPs

In the US study discussed above (Johnson et al., 2010), the SBD question identified 98% (346/354) of women at risk for an AEP, while only 59% of the women reported that they drank ≥ 8 SDs in a week on average. In the Russian study (Balachova et al., in press), an SBD question identified 99% (683/689) of the women at risk, while only 8% of women reported that they drank ≥ 8

SDs in a week on average. The sizeable difference between the two studies when comparing the at-risk drinking criterion average (weekly drinking ≥ 8 SDs) suggests that the binge drinking risk criterion is more sensitive than the weekly average criterion (Balachova et al., 2012; Keenan, Grundy, Kenward, & Leon, 2014).

2.3.3   Quick Drinking Screen

The Quick Drinking Screen (QDS) is one of many quantity-frequency measures (reviewed in Sobell & Sobell, 1992). The QDS is a self-report summary drinking measure that collects aggregate drinking data for four drinking variables, including a binge drinking question for both clinical and nonclinical drinkers (Dum et al., 2009; Roy et al., 2008; Sobell et al., 2003). Data from the QDS and Timeline Follow-Back (TLFB) representing the past 90 days were compared in a sample of women known to be at risk of an AEP to determine if the two drinking assessment methods yielded equivalent estimates of women at risk (Dum et al., 2009). The three QDS questions evaluated were (a) "How many days per week out of the past 90 did you drink any alcohol?"; (b) "On average, on days when you did drink, how many standard drinks did you drink in a day?"; and (c) "In the past 90 days, how many days did you drink 5 or more standard drinks in one day?" The women's answers to the three QDS questions, which were compared with their responses on their 90-day TLFB calendar, were highly similar. Similar results were found in the sample of Russian women comparing an SBD question and 90-day preintervention TLFB data. Of the 689 women known to be at risk of an AEP, the SBD question and the TLFB both correctly identified 99% of all women (Balachova, et al., in press). What these two studies suggest is that the QDS or an SBD question is an acceptable substitute for longer drinking assessment methods, as both identified almost the same number of women whose drinking put them at risk of an AEP compared to the TLFB.

A single binge drinking question identified 99% of all women known to be at risk of an AEP, in two countries

In summary, compared with lengthier drinking assessment methods, an SBD question effectively and efficiently identified 99% of all women (1,034/1,043) in two different countries and cultures, who had previously been determined to be at risk of an AEP. Based on this striking finding, we recommend that physicians and other health and mental care practitioners use an SBD question as a first step to identifying women who are likely to be at risk for an AEP. Women identified by an SBD question can be referred for further screening and a possible brief intervention for an alcohol use disorder.

In some cases, clinicians or researchers may require additional information about women's drinking. For example, in addition to the SBD question, researchers may want to include well-established measures when comparing their results with those of previous studies. Clinicians may require additional documentation of specific patterns or symptoms of drinking to make a diagnosis, or to determine a course of treatment. For these reasons, the Alcohol Use Disorders Identification Test (AUDIT-10), an established and psychometric assessment method, will be reviewed here.

Although several scales are used for brief screening and identification of harmful and hazardous alcohol use, the AUDIT stands out for its psychometric characteristics, convenience, and cross-cultural validation (Reinert & Allen, 2007). The AUDIT, developed as a multinational World Health Organization project, is a brief screening test for the early detection of harmful and hazardous alcohol use in primary health care settings (Saunders, Aasland, Babor, De La Fuente, & Grant, 1993). The 10 questions are scored based on the frequency of the experience (i.e., from 0 = *never* to 4 = *daily use,* maximum score = 40). The AUDIT has been shown to be as good as, or better than, other screening tests (e.g., CAGE, MAST, ADS) in identifying individuals with probable alcohol problems when a cutoff score of ≥ 8 is used (Reinert & Allen, 2007). As noted by the authors, the major differences between the AUDIT and most other similar alcohol screening tests are that it: (a) detects drinkers along the entire drinking severity continuum from mild to moderate to severe; (b) emphasizes hazardous consumption and frequency of intoxication (Questions 1–3) compared with drinking behavior and adverse consequences; (c) uses a time frame that asks questions about both current (i.e., past year) and lifetime use; and (d) importantly, it avoids using a yes/no format; instead it uses Likert rating scales to reduce face validity. While available in several languages, the AUDIT also has good psychometric properties for both men and women, as well as younger drinkers. There is a shorter version of the AUDIT, the AUDIT-C, that has three questions related to quantity and frequency of drinking and is psychometrically similar to the full AUDIT (Dawson, Grant, & Stinson, 2005; Dawson, Smith, Saha, Rubinsky, & Grant, 2012). The AUDIT-10 and AUDIT-C both include a sex-specific binge drinking question that can be used as a stand-alone SBD question.

2.4   Screening for Ineffective Contraception

For most women, using the SBD question will be the most efficient and effective method to determine if a woman is at risk for an AEP. In some cases however, such as when screening women for specific services such as contraception counseling, or a dual-focused AEP prevention program, clinicians may want to screen for pregnancy risk related to ineffective contraception. While alcohol consumption is required to put a woman at risk of an AEP, so is ineffective contraception. As discussed previously, many women of reproductive age who become pregnant do not intend to become pregnant; however, they failed to use any method of contraception or failed to use their method of contraception effectively (e.g., did not take birth control pills every day and took the missed pills a few days later). Such behavior is considered *ineffective contraception* (Project CHOICES Research Group, 2002). The typical way Project CHOICES and similar studies (e.g., Ceperich & Ingersoll, 2011; Floyd et al., 2007; Velasquez, von Sternberg, & Parrish, 2013) have screened for effective contraception is research related and labor intensive and not practical for clinical situations. Screening women for correct use of every method of contraception they have tried can result in accurate classification of women who are at risk for pregnancy (and may not realize it), but it is a lengthy procedure with multiple steps. For this reason, we recommend quicker screens such as the QDS to identify women who are likely at risk for AEP without separately assessing drinking risk and pregnancy risk, unless a complete assessment of reasons for pregnancy risk is required for research or other specific reasons.

2.5   Summary: What Puts Women at Risk for an AEP?

In this chapter, we defined what constitutes a risk for an AEP in terms of two behaviors: at risk drinking and ineffective contraception. Risk drinking (i.e., heavy or binge drinking) occurs in a minority of women in the United States (7–17%; Ingersoll, Ceperich, Nettleman, & Johnson, 2008; Project CHOICES Research Group, 2002). However, binge drinking in the past 30 days occurs more frequently among younger women (i.e., ages 18–25), and women from Native Hawaiian/Pacific Islander and Native American ethnic groups (27% and 19%, respectively). As discussed throughout this chapter, different factors increase the risk for unintended pregnancy (e.g., being between 15 and 19 years of age, with a lower level of education, from certain ethnic groups). When looking at these factors, remember they are correlative not causal (e.g., potentially related to poverty and lack of access to effective methods of contraception).

Although women who are at risk for an AEP come from all sectors of the population, some settings are likely to have more women at risk (e.g., addiction treatment programs, jails, university settings). While most AEP prevention research has been conducted in the United States, we have seen that in one country, Russia, where drinking is generally frequent and high, there is a very high risk of an AEP among women of reproductive age. In addition, some women, especially those with histories of addiction, smoking, mental disorders, physical abuse, multiple partners, and reliance on partners for contraception, are more likely to have higher pregnancy risk rates (e.g., Project CHOICES Research Group, 2002).

While there are no biological tests (e.g., mammograms, blood tests), to screen women at risk for an AEP (due to heavy or binge drinking or ineffective contraception or both), the most efficient and effective screening method, an SBD question, can help health and mental health providers to identify almost all women at risk for AEP who can then be further screened, and if necessary, referred to a brief intervention program.

3

Preventing Alcohol-Exposed Pregnancies

Although the development of FASDs is dependent upon the co-occurrence of drinking alcohol and being pregnant, the preponderance of the FASD literature contains messages like the following: (a) women should not drink if they are trying to become pregnant, (b) there is no safe level of alcohol use when pregnant, (c) women should stop drinking if they are thinking of getting pregnant, and (d) there is no cure for FAS. These messages acknowledge that stopping drinking is hard, and recommend that if a woman needs help to quit she should call Alcoholics Anonymous or go to a treatment center.

3.1   Prevention Dilemma

Although there is nothing wrong with cautioning against drinking when pregnant, this has long been the centerpiece and dominant message of the FASD field. It is also mainly relevant to women who are planning to get pregnant or who are already pregnant. Unfortunately, *most of the messages have ignored the largest segment of women at risk* – those not wanting or planning to get pregnant. A comprehensive approach to AEP prevention needs to emphasize avoiding pregnancies by contracepting effectively. In other words, to prevent an AEP, women can choose to contracept effectively, to not drink at risky levels, or both.

Preventing AEPs is difficult for several reasons
Although most would agree that AEPs are a serious public health problem, the prevention of AEPs has been difficult for several reasons: (a) the drinking threshold above which AEPs can occur may not be diagnostic of an alcohol use disorder or considered problematic by many women (i. e., ≥ 4 SDs on a single day or ≥ 8 SDs per week); (b) almost half of all pregnancies are unplanned; and (c) close to half of women either are not contracepting or are not contracepting effectively (e.g., do not take birth control pills regularly and do not use a backup method).

From an AEP prevention perspective, women who are heterosexually active, not contracepting effectively, and drinking above risk levels but who do not know or do not believe that they may be at risk of becoming pregnant present two challenges. First, as discussed earlier, for women who are using some type of birth control method(s), an important issue is whether they are contracepting effectively. Although many women in this group think they are using birth control methods effectively, the actual methods they are using may not be effective (e.g., the rhythm method). In other cases, a woman might be using an effective method, but not using it properly (e.g., not taking corrective action after forgetting to take a birth control pill). In addition, some women do not use any type of birth control. As previously mentioned, ineffective or no use of birth control accounts for nearly half of all unintended pregnancies in the United States (Finer & Henshaw, 2006; Office of the Surgeon General, 2005). Thus, one major challenge for prevention programs is that there are many women who are at risk of a pregnancy but who fail to recognize their risk.

A second challenge in preventing AEPs relates to what is referred to as risky drinking levels. Although most women when asked if they know that heavy drinking when pregnant will cause harm to an unborn child will say yes, the amount of alcohol that can damage an unborn fetus does not have to meet criteria for an alcohol use disorder (American Psychiatric Association, 2013) or even be considered "heavy drinking." For example, research shows that many women, particularly those who are younger, single, or in college, may drink above risky levels but think their drinking is normative or even less than that of their peers and therefore not be concerned (Neighbors, Larimer, & Lewis, 2004; Winograd & Sher, 2015). Consequently, the challenge is that many women will not view prevention efforts as applicable to them, as they do not believe they are at risk of getting pregnant, nor do they see their drinking as atypical for women their age.

Because many of the traditional FASD messages focus on stopping drinking (e.g., the CDC brochure "Think Before You Drink" includes a statement about attending Alcoholics Anonymous or going for treatment if you cannot stop drinking), these messages do not seem relevant for the large segment of women who do not want to become pregnant, and in fact may evoke resistance. When people feel attacked or labeled, they are likely to respond by counterarguing, generating reasons the label is not applicable to them (Perloff, 2008). In other words, strongly focused alcohol messages such as some of those in FASD prevention efforts may be viewed as not personally relevant by women who are at risk of an AEP if the message is at odds with a woman's beliefs about herself (e.g., "Yes, I drink sometimes, but not that much").

3.2   Primary Prevention Strategies

Initially, most studies focused on identifying critical levels of consumption associated with the severe consequences of FASD. The less severe consequences, once known as *fetal alcohol effects* have received much less attention, perhaps owing to the fact that risky drinking and related consequences have not been well defined (Astley, 2011). However, data from epidemiological studies have changed the FASD field considerably. For many years the focus in the field has been on helping alcohol-dependent women to delay becoming pregnant until stable abstinence has been achieved. More recently the focus has shifted to primary prevention, where women of reproductive age whose drinking places them at risk of an AEP are cautioned about how to avoid an AEP. When we include women who are drinking at risky levels (i.e., ≥ 4 SDs on any one day, or ≥ 8 SDs per week), the population increases substantially. However, because many of these women are not likely to believe their drinking puts them at risk of an AEP, either because their drinking is not diagnostic of a problem or has resulted in few, if any, consequences, this complicates the task of preventing AEPs on a large scale.

Extending the focus to prevent AEPs has created major challenges for prevention programs (e.g., how to screen for AEP risk, how to discuss AEP risk without incurring resistance, how to motivate women to change when they do not believe they are at risk). Because many of these challenges have emerged because of the shift to a primary prevention approach, several new intervention efforts have been designed. As with other public health problems, intervention strategies should be designed with respect to the population served (e.g., college students vs. working women). In 1996, the IOM called for a comprehensive approach to the prevention of AEPs. The report recommended that prevention strategies be undertaken on three levels: *universal prevention strategies* (sometimes called population strategies), *selective prevention strategies*, and *indicated prevention strategies* (sometimes called high-risk strategies).

Universal prevention approaches target the public without regard to differential risk factors. For example, labels that warn pregnant women not to drink alcohol appear on all commercial alcoholic beverages, and presumably those who read the label receive these messages. Although universal strategies have the advantage of targeting the entire population, which is a useful strategy to influence women who a priori cannot be identified as at risk, a disadvantage is that a broad-brush approach is neither intensive nor personalized. Because universal strategies lack a personalized component, many women may discount the information provided as not applicable. Thus, while universal strategies can affect large numbers of people compared with selective strategies, the element of personalized messages or feedback, viewed as important in substance use treatment programs, is missing (Scott-Sheldon, Carey, Elliott, Garey, & Carey, 2014).

The second prevention strategy, selective prevention, targets groups that are thought to be at risk (e.g., college sororities), but does not focus on specific individuals. For example, programs for reducing heavy drinking are implemented on college campuses because students are among the heaviest drinkers (e.g., Borsari & Carey, 2000; Winograd & Sher, 2015). Selective strategies, while targeting particular groups, are also not individualized. Their aim is to reduce heavy drinking across a known group, recognizing that some individuals do not drink at all or do not drink at risky levels. One advantage of selective prevention strategies is that they are more narrowly focused, and usually more intensive than universal strategies. They can also include components specific to the target group. Often these strategies are not personalized. Because not all members of the target group will be at risk, focusing on a specific target group may overlook some individuals who are at risk (e.g., young adults who drink heavily but are not in college).

The third prevention strategy, indicated (or high-risk) prevention, recommended by the IOM, targets only individuals who meet specific criteria for being at risk (e.g., a high school tutoring program that targets students whose performance identifies them as at risk of not graduating). In the present context, women who are not contracepting effectively and are drinking at levels above the criteria for risky drinking would be the focus of such prevention strategies. High-risk prevention strategies usually incorporate more intensive procedures because they target a smaller group of individuals and can be more personalized. As with selective strategies, a drawback is that they may miss some at-risk individuals.

A comprehensive public health approach would include all three types of prevention components. In 2009 the National Task Force on Fetal Alcohol Syndrome and Fetal Alcohol Effects issued a call to action that recommended establishing an integrated system of care for individuals and families affected by FASD (Olson et al., 2009). More recently, an international conference on the prevention of FASD resulted in an International Charter on Prevention of Fetal Alcohol Spectrum Disorder that calls for governments worldwide to take measures to increase public awareness of FASD and of the risks of alcohol use during pregnancy (Jonsson, Salmon, & Warren, 2014). Unfortunately, to date, most work has been limited to the development of the third prevention strategy, high-risk prevention approaches.

In the next part of this chapter, several interventions that were specifically developed for the primary prevention of AEPs are reviewed. Most of these interventions used a selective strategy. Most of these interventions were designed as preconceptional, and thus targeted women who were not pregnant. However, as mentioned earlier, alcohol-related risks extend throughout a woman's entire pregnancy. Therefore, another objective has been to prevent alcohol use by women who have become pregnant. The focus in such cases is clearly to get such women to completely abstain from drinking during their pregnancy.

3.3 Evidence-Based Approaches for the Prevention of AEP

Of all the studies conducted in recent years to reduce AEPs, the most visible and influential is Project CHOICES, a multisite trial (Floyd et al., 2007). The history and development of the Project CHOICES study (Floyd et al., 2007) is described in the Preface. The following review is restricted to the six CHOICES and CHOICES-like studies that (a) used a randomized design, (b) conducted a rigorous follow-up with participants, and (c) reported postintervention outcome data.

For each of the six studies, there is a short description of the intervention and results, as well as a detailed table showing the percentage of women who met different AEP risk reduction thresholds for the postintervention interval (see Tables 2, 3, 4, 5, 6, and 7). To better capture the success of the CHOICES and CHOICES-like studies, Table 8 shows the percentage of women in each study who met the outcome criteria for the overall reduced risk of an AEP at the postintervention follow-up for the CHOICES (experimental) groups and for the control groups. Rather than list all of these outcome findings in the description of each study, we have put each study's major finding in a footnote at the end of each table, along with the overall percentage of participants found for follow-up. All but one of the six studies had a 6-month follow-up interval (Project BALANCE used a 4-month follow-up).

3.3.1 Project CHOICES

The CHOICES intervention was developed in a partnership between investigators from the CDC and from three universities. CHOICES is a prevention program based on the view that women of childbearing age who are not pregnant can be given information with which to make informed choices to avoid an AEP (Project CHOICES Intervention Research Group, 2003; Project CHOICES Research Group, 2002; Floyd et al., 2007).

Women were considered at risk of an AEP if they reported that within the past 3 months they had had vaginal intercourse with a male partner without effective contraception and either consumed ≥ 5 SDs on at least one day or consumed ≥ 8 SDs per week on average. Reduced risk of an AEP was defined as either using effective contraception, drinking below risky levels, or both, since either path would prevent an AEP as defined by this study. The CHOICES intervention was developed and tested against an informational intervention in a RCT with 830 at-risk women in six different settings (e.g., jail, primary medical care, brief outpatient). At a 9-month follow-up, significantly more women who participated in the CHOICES intervention compared with those in the informational intervention were no longer at risk of AEP.

Having met a set of rigorous peer-review criteria, Project CHOICES was recently selected for inclusion in the National Registry of Evidence-Based Programs and Practices (http://nrepp.samhsa.gov/ViewIntervention.

The CHOICES intervention is a primary prevention intervention

aspx?id=348). The CHOICES efficacy study was also given the 2008 Charles C. Shepard Science Award for excellence in prevention and control by the CDC, and was cited by the Agency for Toxic Substances and Disease Registry (ATSDR) as the most outstanding peer-reviewed research paper published by CDC/ATSDR scientists during the preceding year. The CDC Web page describes Project CHOICES as "a model program embraced by researchers and used in other federal initiatives" (http://www.cdc.gov/ncbddd/fasd/research-preventing.html).

CHOICES Rationale

CHOICES works with women before they become pregnant

The CHOICES intervention was designed to prevent an AEP, by giving women the *CHOICE* of changing one of two different behaviors or both (i.e., contracepting effectively or reducing drinking below AEP risk levels, or both). The rationale for giving women the choice of which behavior to change (or both) is that many either do not want to change or do not see a need to change both behaviors to prevent an AEP. Thus, for women who do not want to get pregnant, but who also do not want to reduce or change their drinking, they can choose to contracept effectively. On the other hand, for women who decide to reduce or stop drinking for personal reasons, they can elect to not use any form of birth control. In other words, women have the choice to change one or both target behaviors to prevent an AEP. Regardless of how it is achieved, the important outcome is the prevention of an AEP.

Women have the choice to change one or both of two target behaviors: reduce/stop drinking or contracept effectively

Because the majority of women at risk of an AEP are not only not seeking help, but also may not think they are at risk, a key component of the CHOICES intervention is motivational interviewing (MI; Miller & Rollnick, 2012). Developed initially for working with individuals with alcohol use disorders, MI is a set of communication skills that can best be described as a directive client-centered interaction with the objective of creating a climate in which clients feel comfortable talking about their risky behaviors. The interaction was designed to be collaborative, nonjudgmental, nonconfrontational, and supportive, and to help the patient give voice to the change process (see the Clinical Pearl "Discussing the Two Target Behaviors in Project CHOICES"). When a patient chooses his or her own change process, it avoids having the practitioner give lectures. For women who are not ready or uncertain about the need to change their behavior(s) to prevent an AEP, the conversation is designed to help them address their ambivalence, while minimizing resistance.

Although MI was developed in the early 1980s for use with clients with substance use disorders (Miller & Rollnick, 2012), today it has been extended to a variety of health and mental health problems with patients who are ambivalent about changing risky or problem behaviors (Rollnick, Miller, & Butler, 2008). Studies that have compared MI versus traditional confrontational approaches have consistently found that MI studies result in less resistance, increased compliance, lower dropout rates, better attendance during treatment, better treatment outcomes, and higher client satisfaction (Martino, Carroll, O'Malley, & Rounsaville, 2000; Swanson, Pantalon, & Cohen,1999).

Clinical Pearl
Discussing the Two Target Behaviors in Project CHOICES

Effective Use of Birth Control Methods

Practitioner: If you don't use birth control pills as prescribed, what do you think might happen? **[By asking the patient to give voice to her thoughts, the practitioner avoids lecturing the patient]**

Patient: Well. I could get pregnant. **[Patient gives voice to the change process]**

Practitioner: What would it be like for you to have a child while you are in graduate school?

Patient: It would really delay my plans for getting a job, and my husband and I aren't ready for a family.

Reduced Alcohol Use

Practitioner: I know you said you only drink five or six drinks once a month. Because you are not using any birth control, what could happen if you drink five or six drinks just on 1 or 2 days?

Client: I could get pregnant, and I guess the alcohol wouldn't be good for my baby. Right?

Practitioner: It sounds like you are not convinced that a few heavier drinking days could affect your unborn child. How do you think alcohol affects an unborn child?

Client: Probably not good?

Practitioner: Right, even a few drinks or a few days of drinking, especially early in a woman's pregnancy, can cause some problems. How do you think we can help you prevent your child from developing any problems?

In summary, the CHOICES intervention was designed to be motivational in nature, and to use strategies consistent with brief cognitive behavior interventions for alcohol problems. CHOICES interventions share some of the same challenges (e.g., clients are ambivalent about changing) posed by interventions designed to encourage heavy drinkers to reduce or stop their drinking (Carey, Carey, Maisto, & Henson, 2006; Sobell & Sobell 1993).

Intervention Components and Resources

Consistent with the intent to disseminate the results of the CHOICES study, all of the materials used in the five-session CHOICES curriculum (four counseling and one contraception counseling session; each session averaging 45–60 min) are available at no cost from the CDC (http://www.cdc.gov/ncbddd/ fasd/freematerials.html; see also Appendices 3 and 4 in this book for example excercises from the CHOICES intervention). The CHOICES curriculum includes (a) a *Facilitator Guide for Trainers,* (b) a *Counselor Manual,* and (c) *Client Workbook.* The CHOICES intervention and how to implement it are further described in detail in Velasquez et al. (2010). Because many of the other interventions reviewed in this section are similar to, or adaptations of, the CHOICES intervention, the main CHOICES intervention procedures are summarized in the following paragraphs.

As mentioned earlier, MI was first developed for working with individuals who feel ambivalent or uncertain about changing, and that makes the approach well suited for the prevention of AEPs. Because the objective of a motivational approach is to engage people in an open dialogue about their behavior, an important aspect of an MI style is to not be confrontational or judgmental. Motivational interactions are also intended to help people understand their mixed feelings about changing (i.e., their ambivalence). Helping people understand why they are ambivalent about changing often involves having them looking at both sides of their behavior – that is, both the good and bad aspects of continuing as well as changing their current behavior. Often practitioners use a decisional balance exercise, as discussed below, that helps patients sort out their feelings, which in turn often helps them feel more prepared to make a decision about changing.

Another way the CHOICES intervention is motivational is that it provides women with personalized feedback about their drinking and how it places them at risk of an AEP should they become pregnant, and also about how their current contraceptive practices place them at risk of getting pregnant. This feedback was designed to be educational and to encourage a continued dialogue about behavioral change; in this case, it involves two behaviors (i.e., risky drinking and ineffective or no contraception) that place a woman at risk of an AEP. As shown in the Clinical Pearl "Sample Script for How to Provide Personalized Feedback," the feedback is presented in an objective, nonjudgmental manner, where the woman is asked to give voice to what might happen if she does or does not change. Note that scare tactics, moralizing, and lecturing are avoided when using MI. The key to presenting information relates to using a motivational style that elicits the patient's perspective (Miller & Rollnick, 2012). One way to elicit "change talk" (i.e., client self-motivating statements of reasons or desires to change) is to ask patients about their reactions to the feedback.

Clinical Pearl
Sample Script for How to Provide Personalized Feedback

In sessions that provide information and feedback, clients are invited to comment on the information provided, which in turn removes the lecture component of providing information. Reflective listening can be used with clients' verbal and nonverbal responses to feedback – for example: (a) It sounds like you are surprised about what the feedback says; (b) I am sensing that this surprises you, as you thought you were contracepting effectively; and (c) We have prepared some information about what you told us about your drinking in the last 90 days. In looking at these graphs, where does yours fit in?

Practitioner: Do you mind if we talk about some of the questionnaires you completed last week, for a few minutes? **[Asking permission]**

Patient: Sure.

Practitioner: We prepared these graphs for you. In looking at them and seeing what other women your age drink, where does your drinking fit it?

Patient: Well it looks like it is in the high category. How can that be? My friends drink more than me.

Practitioner: It sounds like you are surprised. I remember that you also told us that you sometimes don't use birth control when having intercourse. Although your drinking might not seem like a lot, when you don't use any birth control and drink, it puts you at risk of becoming pregnant.

Patient: Wow, that is not what I want to happen, as I need to finish college.

Practitioner: You sound surprised, and a baby at this time would interfere with you completing school right now. **[Reflection]**

Patient: For sure.

Practitioner: Would you be interested in learning about effective methods of birth control and a list of referrals? **[Asking permission]**

Patient: Yes, that sounds good.

The CHOICES intervention also asks women to complete and discuss decisional balance exercises for their alcohol use and birth control practices. These exercises provide a structured way to evaluate the pros and cons of changing their drinking and their contraceptive practices (see Appendix 4). Such exercises help people understand why they might be ambivalent about changing (Sobell & Sobell, 2011). The decisional balance exercises also generate a rich dialogue between the practitioner and the woman at risk.

Self-monitoring (Korotitsch & Nelson-Gray, 1999), a very common behavioral tool, was also used in CHOICES. Throughout the intervention the women were asked to keep a daily log of both target behaviors: drinking and birth control practices. The logs, which are discussed at the start of each session, provide a systematic and structured opportunity for women to report any drinking and birth control use since the last session. They also allow practitioners to give supportive feedback for changes in one or both behaviors that have occurred since the previous session.

Another critical component of the CHOICES intervention has been allowing women to set their own goals. Having women choose their own goals and develop their own change plans is consistent with a cognitive social learning theory that suggests people will be more committed to goals that they set for themselves (Bandura, 2001). Choice, for many people, can be empowering.

When a woman sets her own goals, this means she can decide to contracept effectively, as well as not to change her drinking. Likewise, a woman can decide to reduce or stop drinking and not use birth control. When viewed from an overall health perspective *both options are effective from the standpoint of preventing an AEP*. During the four CHOICES counseling sessions, the women were able to obtain advice on choosing birth control strategies as well as to discuss ways to reduce or stop drinking. However, the choice of whether to change, and how to change, was left with each woman.

Selection of Participants for the CHOICES and CHOICES-Like RCTs

In each of the six CHOICES RCTs, all participants had to be at risk of an AEP. Based on their self-reports, all of the women had to meet the following criteria during the baseline interval which was typically 90 days prior to the start of each study: (a) being of reproductive age (18 through 44 years); (b) engaged in heterosexual vaginal intercourse; (c) using no or ineffective contraceptive methods; and (d) consuming an average of ≥ 8 SDs (1 SD = 14 g absolute ethanol per week and/or having engaged in binge drinking (i.e., ≥ 5 or ≥ 4 SDs on at least 1 day). When the original CHOICES study was conducted, the existing epidemiological data suggested a binge drinking risk criterion of ≥ 5 SDs on 1 day (Jacobson & Jacobson, 1999). More recently, the CDC adopted a threshold level of ≥ 4 SDs on 1 day (Bertrand, Floyd, & Weber, 2005; Sayal, et al., 2009). The ≥ 4 SD criterion was adopted from a broader perspective on drinking by women in general, drawing upon epidemiological studies that examined drinking levels as related to several different alcohol-related outcomes (e.g., dependence, several health problems, impaired driving; Dawson, 2000).

Four of the studies used the ≥ 4 SD binge definition, and two (i.e., Project CHOICES and Project Healthy CHOICES; Sobell et al., 2015) used ≥ 5 SDs. The two slightly different criteria should not affect any results or conclusions. Using the binge drinking criterion of ≥ 4 SDs to screen women would have included all women who would have met the ≥ 5 SD criterion. Risky drinking levels have been defined by the NIAAA (2005) as consuming ≥ 8 SDs per week and/or ≥ 4 SDs on 1 day.

Results of Project CHOICES

Table 2 shows the percentage of women in Project CHOICES who met different risk reduction thresholds at 3, 6, and 9 months postintervention. At the 9-month follow-up, 69% of women in the experimental group had an overall reduced risk of an AEP. Of the three routes to reduced risk of an AEP (i.e., reduced drinking, using effective contraception, or both), most women chose to contracept effectively. Nearly half of the women (47.3%) had reduced their drinking and were also using effective contraception.

Table 2
Project CHOICES: Proportion of Participants Meeting Risk Reduction Thresholds for Targeted Behaviors and Reduced Risk for AEP (3, 6, and 9 Months Postintervention; N = 830)

Risk Outcomes %[a]	3 Months		6 Months		9 Months	
	IO [a] (n = 333)[†]	IPC [b] (n = 332)[†]	IO (n = 305)	IPC (n = 299)	IO (n = 302)	IPC (n = 291)
Reduced risky drinking[c]	30.3%	42.2%	32.5%	42.4%	40.4%	48.8%
Effective contraception	28.4%	45.8%	32.8%	47.7%	38.7%	56.3%
Reduced risk for AEP	45.6%	63.6%	46.9%	63.9%	54.3%	69.1%

Note. All follow-up intervals were 90 days from the end of each follow-up period. The variable Reduced Risk for AEP includes both reduced risky drinking and effective contraception outcomes during each of the three 90-day follow-up intervals; 80.1%, 72.8%, and 71.4% of all participants were found for follow-up at 3, 6, and 9 months, respectively. For all measures and at all follow-up intervals, significantly more women in the IPC group were not at risk of an AEP as compared with women in the IO Group ($p < .05$) for both the completers and intent-to-treat analyses. AEP = alcohol-exposed pregnancy; IO = information only (control group); IPC = information plus counseling (intervention group).
[a]Sample sizes per cell may vary slightly from the overall (N) due to missing data for some cells at a given follow-up point.
[b]Reduced risk drinking includes both alcohol use less than 8 drinks per week and no binge drinking[a]
[c]Binge drinking means ≥ 4 drinks per day.
Reprinted from the American Journal of Preventive Medicine, 22(1), Floyd, R. L., Sobell, M., Velasquez, M. M., Ingersoll, K., Nettleman, M., Sobell, L., . . . Project CHOICES Efficacy Study Group, Preventing alcohol-exposed pregnancies: A randomized controlled trial, pp. 1–10. © 2007 with permission from Elsevier.

3.3.2   Project BALANCE

Project BALANCE, an acronym for Birth Control and Alcohol Awareness: Negotiating Choices Effectively, was modeled after Project CHOICES and designed for college students 18 to 24 years of age (Ceperich & Ingersoll, 2011). The BALANCE intervention consisted of a single session, and the experimental group provided participants with personalized feedback using a MI style. The RCT involved 207 college students at risk of an AEP. The CHOICES (experimental) intervention was compared to a control intervention that consisted of an informational brochure on women's health.

Table 3 shows the percentage of women in Project BALANCE that met different AEP risk reduction thresholds for the 90 days prior to the 4-month follow-up. At the 4-month postintervention follow-up, significantly more women in the BALANCE experimental group had a higher overall reduced risk of an AEP compared with women in the informational control group (79% vs. 65%, respectively). Differences in reduced risky drinking reduction and effective contraception were, however, not statistically significant between the two groups (i.e., the groups only differed when reduced drinking and effective contraception were combined). As in the original CHOICES study, more women in both intervention groups achieved risk reduction by improving their contraceptive practices than by reducing their drinking. From an implementation standpoint, the BALANCE experimental group involved considerably fewer resources and less time compared with the original CHOICES information plus counseling (IPC) experimental group. The very high percentage of women who were college students (79%) who achieved an overall AEP risk reduction at the 6-month follow-up could possibly reflect the fact that college students are motivated to avoid pregnancy and thus an AEP – a hypothesis that is supported by the students in the BALANCE control group (informational brochure) having achieved a 65% AEP risk reduction.

Table 3
Percentage of Female College Students in Project BALANCE Meeting AEP Risk Reduction Thresholds at 4 Months Postintervention (N = 207)

Type of risk outcome	Intervention type	
	MI + Feedback (n = 101)	Information control (n = 106)
Reduced risky drinking[a]	33.7%	22.4%
Effective contraception	68.7%	55.1%
Overall reduced risk of AEP[b]	79.8%	65.1%

Note. 90.2% of all participants were found for followed up at 4 months. The motivational interviewing (MI) + feedback group had significantly more women not at risk at the 4-month follow-up than the information control group ($p < .02$), but the groups did not differ significantly on reduced risk drinking or effective contraception. AEP = alcohol-exposed pregnancy.
[a]Defined as ≤ 7 drinks per week or ≤ 3 drinks on all days during the 90 days from the date of the 4-month follow-up.
[b]Overall reduced risk of an AEP outcome includes both reduced risky drinking and effective contraception outcome.
Adapted from Ceperich & Ingersoll (2011).

3.3.3   Project CHOICES and Healthy Moms

The Project CHOICES and Healthy Mom's study was an RCT evaluating the efficacy of a CHOICES-like intervention to reduce the risk of an AEP. The intervention combined the researchers' previous brief alcohol interventions with women with the Project CHOICES intervention. A two-session intervention was conducted using a MI counseling style and personalized feedback, a decisional balance exercise, and other features of the CHOICES intervention, including a participant workbook (mailed to telephone participants). While both groups were given the same CHOICES-like intervention, the groups differed in whether the intervention was delivered by phone or in person (Wilton et al., 2013). A total of 131 women who were at risk of an AEP participated, with 68 assigned to the telephone group and 63 to the in-person group.

Table 4 shows the percentage of women who met the three AEP risk reduction thresholds at the 6-month postintervention follow-up. Follow-up data are presented for the 90 days prior to the 6-month follow-up. As in other studies, women in both groups reduced their drinking and improved their contraceptive practices. Although there were no significant differences between the CHOICES phone and in-person modalities, this study demonstrated that a CHOICES phone intervention can be used with women living in rural areas and for those who might have trouble attending in-person sessions (e.g., due to a lack of transportation or child care).

Table 4
Percentage of Women in Project CHOICES and Healthy Moms Meeting AEP Risk Reduction Thresholds at 6 Months Postintervention Using an Intent-to-Treat Analysis (N = 131)

Type of risk outcome	Intervention type	
	Two phone sessions (n = 68)	Two sessions in person (n = 63)
Reduced risky drinking[a]	10%	12%
Effective contraception	38%	49%
Overall reduced risk of AEP[b]	44%	52%

Note. 67.9% of all participants were found for follow-up at the 6 months. The two groups did not differ on any of three risk outcome measures. AEP = alcohol-exposed pregnancy.
[a]Defined as ≤ 7 drinks per week or ≤ 3 drinks on all days during the 90 days prior to the 6-month follow-up date.
[b]Overall reduced risk of an AEP outcome includes both reduced risky drinking and effective contraception outcomes.
Adapted from Wilton et al. (2013).

3.3.4 CHOICES Plus

This study had two primary objectives: The first was to adapt the CHOICES intervention for use in primary care settings in a managed health care system. The second was to extend the CHOICES intervention to the prevention of tobacco-exposed pregnancies (TEPs). The CHOICES Plus intervention was two sessions (45 min each) plus a referral to a primary care provider for a contraception consultation. The intervention also included a referral to a smoking cessation program. This RCT compared the CHOICES Plus (CP) intervention with a brief advice (BA) group that received advice and educational material about risky drinking, smoking, and contraception. This latter group also received information about specific risk behaviors and women's health.

Table 5 shows the percentage of women in the CP group who met different AEP risk reduction thresholds at the 3-, 6-, and 9-month postintervention follow-ups. Data are reported for the 90-days prior to each of the three follow-up intervals. At the 9-month follow-up, CP participants had significantly less risk of an AEP for all three reduced risk outcomes than participants in the BA group. Finally, the CP women had a greater probability of a reduced risk for a TEP at 9 months than women in the BA group.

Table 5
Percentage of Women in CHOICES Plus Meeting AEP Risk Reduction Thresholds at 3, 6, and 9 Months Postintervention ($N = 261$)

Type of risk outcome	Intervention type					
	BA ($n = 119$)	CP ($n = 127$)	BA ($n = 117$)	CP ($n = 122$)	BA ($n = 115$)	CP ($n = 120$)
	3 Months		6 Months		9 Months	
Reduced risky drinking[a]	16.8%	33.9%	17.1%	38.8%	25.2%	38.5%
Effective contraception	11.8%	34.6%	18.8%	41.8%	22.6%	46.7%
Overall reduced risk of AEP[b]	25.2%	52.0%	29.9%	58.2%	37.4%	60.8%

Note. 87%, 89%, and 95% of participants were found for follow-up at 3, 6, and 9 months, respectively. At the 3-, 6- and 9-month follow-ups, the two groups differ significantly ($p < .05$) on all three outcome variables. AEP = alcohol-exposed pregnancy; BA = brief advice group; CP = CHOICES Plus group.
[a]Defined as ≤ 7 drinks per week or ≤ 3 drinks on all days during the 90 days prior to the follow-up interval.
[b]Overall reduced risk of an AEP outcome includes both reduced risky drinking and effective contraception outcomes.
Adapted from Velasquez et al. (2014).

3.3.5   Project EARLY

A serious impediment to the dissemination of effective programs involves demands that the interventions place upon both health care practitioners and their patients. For example, although the availability of a detailed counselor's manual and client workbook greatly facilitates the conduct of the CHOICES intervention, implementing the full intervention requires five different sessions. Because many women at risk of an AEP either do not believe they are at risk of pregnancy or do not feel their occasional heavy drinking is problematic, it may be that such women would not attend five sessions. Moreover, in clinical practice versus a research setting, the services would presumably involve a cost for both practitioners and patients. Therefore, it is important to identify the briefest intervention and the components of the intervention that will have substantial benefit while requiring the fewest resources and shortest time commitment.

In an effort to economize on the intervention without sacrificing effectiveness, Project EARLY involved testing a low resource, one-session version of the CHOICES intervention (Ingersoll, Ceperich, Hettema, Farrell-Carnahan, & Penberthy, 2013). The participants were women from the community who were at risk of an AEP and who volunteered for the study. Following a 75-min assessment, participants were randomly assigned to an informational video condition, an informational brochure condition, or the EARLY intervention condition, with the relevant treatment procedures implemented

Table 6
Percentage of Women in Project EARLY Meeting AEP Risk Reduction Thresholds at 3 and 6 Months Postintervention (N =217)

Type of risk outcome	MI, assessment feedback, education, no contraception (n =58)	Information video (n =56)	Information brochure (n = 67)	MI, assessment feedback, education, no contraception (n = 49)	Information video (n = 47)	Information brochure (n = 62)
		3 Months			6 Months	
Reduced risk drinking[a]	16.8%	19.6%	16.4%	24.5%	19.2%	28.6%
Effective contraception	19.0%	10.7%	13.6%	33.3%	23.4%	23.7%
Overall reduced risk of AEP[b]	34.5%	30.4%	28.4%	52.0%	36.2%	45.2%

Note. 84.3% and 75.6% of all participants were found for follow-up at 3 and 6 months, respectively. The three groups did not differ (*p* > .05) at 3 or 6 months on any of three risk outcome measures. AEP = alcohol-exposed pregnancy; MI = motivational interviewing.
[a]Defined as ≤ 7 drinks per week and ≤ 3 drinks on all days during the 90 days prior to the 3-month follow-up. The only place the authors reported risky drinking was in Table 4 in their article where they used the CHOICES criterion of ≤ 4 drinks for comparison with CHOICES and BALANCE. (In EARLY, they used ≤ 3 drinks as a cutoff for reduced drinking.)
[b]Overall reduced risk of an AEP outcome includes both reduced risky drinking and effective contraception outcomes.
Adapted from Ingersoll et al. (2013).

at the conclusion of the assessment. The 60-min EARLY session focused on using MI, assessment feedback, and education without contraception counseling. Follow-up, conducted at 3 and 6 months post baseline, retrospectively assessed behavior during the 90-day period preceding the follow-up point. Besides using regular outcome criteria (dichotomous classification of at-risk or not at-risk of AEP), the study also included measures of improvement (e.g., percentage of days with unprotected sexual encounters). Table 6 shows the percentage of women in Project EARLY who met different AEP risk reduction thresholds at the 3- and 6-month postintervention follow-ups. As in the other studies, the main change was effective contraception. In addition, estimated effect sizes showed that participants who received the EARLY intervention had a slightly lower risk of AEP and a slightly lower rate of ineffective contraception than those who received the video or brochure intervention. The effect sizes were not statistically significant, however, possibly due to limited sample sizes. The groups did not differ significantly in terms of reduced drinking, which in this study was measured by mean SDs per drinking day. Although the EARLY intervention seemed to be less potent than the other CHOICES interventions, the intervention still could have utility in settings where time and resources are limited.

3.3.6   Project Healthy CHOICES

Project Healthy CHOICES, based on the CHOICES intervention, was a two-group RCT for women who were at risk of an AEP (Sobell et al., 2015; Sobell, Sobell, Johnson, & Bolton, 2007). Women voluntarily responded to advertisements (e.g., newspapers, radio, postal flyers) for the study. They were screened using the same criteria as Project CHOICES: drinking at risky levels (≥ 8 SDs per week or engaged in binge drinking of ≥ 5 SDs on at least 1 day), sexually active, and not using or ineffectively using contraceptive methods. The study was conducted entirely by mail; all assessment and intervention materials were sent to participants via the US Postal Service. Participants also returned their assessment materials by mail. Participants were able to request materials in Spanish or English.

Participants assigned to the experimental group (personalized feedback group) were sent personalized motivational feedback materials based on their assessment answers about their alcohol and contraceptive use. Participants in the control group (standard treatment group) only received "Think Before You Drink," a brochure developed by the CDC that describes what FAS is and how to prevent it; the simple message conveyed is "avoid drinking during pregnancy" with no information about how to contracept effectively. The CDC brochure was selected as a proxy for treatment as usual, as it is freely available in the community and on the CDC website in both English ("Think Before You Drink") and Spanish ("Piénselo Antes de Beber").

A total of 354 women participated in the study. At the 6-month follow-up, 92% (325/354) of the participants were interviewed. As shown in Table 7, while 100% of all participants were at risk of an AEP at the start of the study, at the 6-month follow-up, 60.0% (195/325) had reduced their overall risk during the entire 6-month postintervention interval. Although 63% (103/164) of the participants in the personalized feedback condition were not at risk during the entire 6-month follow-up, 57% (92/161) of those who received the standard CDC FAS brochure also were no longer at risk. This finding suggests that participating in the screening and assessment procedures and being given a very simple brochure were sufficient to prompt behavioral changes in over half of all of the women. In Project Healthy CHOICES, as with the other CHOICES studies, the predominant way women lessened their risk of an AEP was through effective contraception.

Based on several recent studies, the best way to prevent AEPs is to prevent unintended pregnancies

An important finding is that the predominant way women in all six CHOICES and CHOICES-like studies reduced their risk of an AEP was by contracepting effectively. Although the drinking of the majority of these non-pregnant women was defined as at risk for an AEP, for the majority it would not necessarily have qualified them for an alcohol use disorder diagnosis. The fact that the majority of women *chose* to avoid an AEP by contracepting effectively rather than changing their drinking is consistent with the interview

Table 7
Percentage of Female College Students and Nonstudents in Project Healthy CHOICES Meeting AEP Risk Reduction Thresholds at 6 Months Postintervention (*N* = 325)

Type of risk outcome	Student status and intervention type			
	Students CDC FAS brochure (Control, *n* = 67)	Students personalized feedback brochures for alcohol and contraception (Experimental, *n* = 68)	Nonstudents CDC FAS brochure (Control, *n* = 94)	Nonstudents personalized feedback brochures for alcohol and contraception (Experimental, *n* =96)
Reduced risk drinking[a]	20.90%	19.12%	18.09%	15.63%
Effective contraception	56.72%	72.06%	44.68%	42.71%
Overall reduced risk of AEP[b]	65.67%	79.41%	51.06%	51.04%

Note: Follow-up data were gathered for 91.81% of the participants at 6 months; 90.1% of all participants were found for follow-up. The 6-month follow-up included 180 days. The experimental and control groups did not differ significantly ($p > .05$) on any of the three risk outcome measures. The experimental student group differed significantly ($p < .05$) from the other three groups on overall reduced risk of an AEP. AEP = alcohol-exposed pregnancy; CDC = Centers for Disease Control and Prevention; FAS = fetal alcohol syndrome.
[a]Defined as ≤ 7 drinks per week and ≤ 4 drinks on all 180 days during the 6-month follow-up interval.
[b]Overall reduced risk of an AEP outcome includes both reduced risk drinking risk and effective contraception outcomes.
Adapted from Sobell, Sobell, Johnson, & Bolton (2007) and Sobell et al. (2015).

responses from women in Project Healthy CHOICES (Sobell et al., 2015). In that study, at the assessment, all 354 participants were asked to use a 5-point scale (1 = *not important,* 2 = *slightly important,* 3 = *somewhat important,* 4 = *very important,* 5 = *extremely important*) to evaluate the importance of not becoming pregnant and the need to change their drinking at the present time. For the question about the importance of *not becoming pregnant at the present time,* their mean response was 4.33, which suggested it was very important for them to not get pregnant at the time they entered the study. On the other hand, when they were asked how important it was *to reduce your alcohol use at the present time,* their mean response was 2.03, suggesting that they felt much less strongly (i.e., it was "slightly important") about the need to reduce their drinking when the study started.

Finally, Table 8 shows the percentage of women in the six CHOICES and CHOICES-like studies who met the overall reduced risk of AEP criteria at the 6-month postintervention follow-up (one study used a 4-month follow-up; Ceperich & Ingersoll, 2011). For each of the six studies, data are presented

Table 8
Percentage of Women in Six CHOICES and CHOICES-like Studies Who Met
Overall Reduced Risk of AEP at 6 Months Postintervention for the CHOICES
(Experimental) and Standard FASD (Control) Intervention Groups

Type of CHOICES Study	Overall reduced risk of AEP
Project CHOICES	
IO (*n* = 305)	46.9%
IPC (*n* = 299)	**63.9%**
Project BALANCE [a]	
MI + feedback (*n* = 101)	**79.8%**
Information control (*n* = 106)	65.1%
Project Healthy Moms and CHOICES [b]	
Two phone sessions (*n* = 68)	44.0%
Two In-person sessions (*n* = 63)	**52.0%**
Project CHOICES Plus	
BATA (*n* = 117)	29.9%
CP Plus (*n* = 122)	**58.2%**
Project EARLY	
MI, assessment feedback, Education (no contraception) (n = 49)	**43.9%**
Information video (*n* = 47)	36.2%
Information brochure (*n* = 62)	46.0%
Project Healthy CHOICES	
Students: standard CDC brochure (*n* = 67)	65.7%
Students: personalized AEP feedback (*n* = 68)	**79.4%**
Nonstudents: standard CDC brochure (*n* = 94)	51.1%
Nonstudents: personalized AEP feedback (*n* = 96)	**51.0%**

Note: For each study, two groups are listed. The CHOICES or CHOICES-like group (**experimental**) is in **bold**, and the comparison or standard FASD (control) intervention group is not. AEP = alcohol-exposed pregnancy; BATA = Brief Advice, Treatment as Usual; CDC = Centers for Disease Control and Prevention; CP = Project CHOICES Plus; IO = information only group; IPC = information plus counseling group; MI = motivational interviewing.
[a]4-month follow-up only.
[b]Data are presented for participants in an intent to treat analysis.

for two intervention groups: the experimental (i.e., CHOICES intervention) group and the control (standard FASD care). While all of the CHOICES or CHOICES-like interventions (experimental groups) had higher success rates than the standard control interventions, an equally important finding was that all control groups showed substantial overall reduced risk outcomes. Remembering that all women in Table 8 (control and experimental) were at risk when they entered their respective studies, the percentages of reduced risk for an AEP postintervention for all control groups is impressive. Nonetheless, the percentage change is even more remarkable for the CHOICES and CHOICES-like interventions.

3.4   Secondary Prevention: Minimizing Alcohol-Related Harm During Pregnancy

Although the focus of this book is on preventing AEPs, here we briefly discuss secondary prevention studies so that practitioners will have some background and understanding of how to work with women who continue to drink during their pregnancy. The six CHOICES interventions just discussed were designed not only to prevent the risk of an AEP but to do so with a dual focus (i.e., an AEP can be prevented by not becoming pregnant, by not drinking at risk levels, or both). However, once conception occurs, there are still opportunities to minimize the risk of harm to the fetus. This is important because surveys by the CDC have found that more than 12% of pregnant women reported drinking some alcohol during their pregnancy, and approximately 2% reported binge drinking (i.e., ≥ 5 SDs on 1 day; CDC, 2009).

In one study, 250 pregnant women who reported drinking alcohol over the past 6 months were randomly assigned to one of two groups: 2-hr assessment only or assessment plus brief intervention (Chang, Wilkins-Haug, Berman, & Goetz, 1999). Unlike the CHOICES-like interventions that placed a heavy emphasis on MI, the intervention was a brief primary care intervention focused on women who had alcohol problems. The procedures were developed and used in World Health Organization studies (World Health Organization Brief Intervention Study Group, 1996). The 45-min brief intervention session reviewed a woman's health and lifestyle issues with her and then asked her for a drinking goal. The women were also given a manual, *How to Prevent Alcohol-Related Problems*, to take home and read.

Follow-up was gathered from 99% of the participants. Of those who were abstinent at the start of the study, significantly more women in the intervention group maintained abstinence up through their delivery. While some who had not been abstinent at the start of treatment showed declines in drinking, 17% reported an increase in drinking following the assessment. There was no significant difference in drinking reduction between the brief intervention and the assessment-only group, possibly because the 2-hr assessment may have catalyzed a reduction in drinking. This hypothesis has support in the alcohol treatment literature (Clifford, Maisto, & Davis, 2007; Epstein et al., 2005).

In another study, O'Connor and Whaley (2007) randomly assigned 345 pregnant women to an assessment-only condition or to a 10- to 15-min scripted brief intervention. All women received a "comprehensive" assessment. The brief intervention, which was conducted by a nutritionist, included education and feedback, cognitive behavior procedures, goal setting, and a contract. While women in both conditions reduced their drinking, those in the brief intervention group were 5 times more likely to report abstinence after the intervention compared with women in the assessment-only condition. The authors suggested that women in the assessment-only group might have reduced their drinking for two reasons: (a) they wanted to give birth to a healthy baby, and

(b) the amount of time the nutritionist spent with them. Again, it is possible that the assessment was reactive and prompted the women to reduce their drinking.

In a small pilot study ($N = 42$) conducted several years ago, pregnant women who reported drinking were randomly assigned to receive either (a) information about the risks of their drinking during pregnancy, or (b) a 1-hr empathic, client-centered directive MI that focused on the health of a woman's unborn baby (Handmaker, Miller, & Manicke, 1999). At a 2-month follow-up, there were no differences between groups for overall alcohol use or abstinent days. However, 81% (34/42) of the women who remained in the study showed a significant reduction in drinking. Results also showed that for women who had reached higher estimated BACs when they drank prior to the intervention, those in the MI condition showed significantly lower BACs than those assigned to the information condition group. Although there was improvement for both groups, the authors noted that after the intervention, more than half of all women in both groups continued to drink, but at lower levels.

In another small-sample study, Tzilos, Sokol, and Ondersma (2011) evaluated a computer-delivered intervention for alcohol use by pregnant women at an inner city prenatal care clinic. After completing a 40-min computer-administered assessment, the women were randomized to either a computer-delivered intervention ($n = 27$) or to an assessment-only condition ($n = 23$). The intervention was individually tailored with respect to whether the woman planned to cut down or quit drinking. Those who were ready to change participated in goal setting, whereas those who were not planning to quit or cut down were directed to a decisional balance exercise and given feedback about their drinking. Those in the intervention condition who had already stopped drinking were directed to a relapse prevention module. Women assigned to the assessment-only condition were administered a series of questions about video entertainment preferences to control for time spent interacting on the computer. At a 1-month follow-up, both groups had reduced their drinking, with only 10% reporting any drinking, whereas at the baseline assessment, 70% reported drinking. Although women in the intervention condition reported positive attitudes toward the intervention, the women who did not get the intervention also reduced their drinking. In this regard, the authors suggested that the 40-min assessment might account for the reduction in drinking by the control group.

In a survey in Minnesota (vs. a clinical study), 683 women who had been pregnant for at least 5 months were interviewed. One question they were asked was if they had received advice from their physician regarding drinking during their recent pregnancy (Jones-Webb, McKiver, Pirie, & Miner, 1999). Women who did not drink or who reported that their physician did not give them advice about their alcohol use were excluded from the study. Survey responses were coded into three categories: (a) advised to stop drinking, (b) advised to reduce their drinking, or (c) told their drinking was okay while pregnant. The study found that drinking during pregnancy was less common among pregnant women who were advised to abstain compared with those advised to reduce their drinking or told their drinking was "okay." Although these findings are not surprising, there are many uncontrolled, potentially confounding variables that might explain the findings (e.g., physicians were self-selected by the women; more health-concerned women may have chosen physicians likely to advise no drinking during pregnancy).

Lastly, a study conducted close to 2 decades ago randomly assigned economically disadvantaged pregnant women attending public health maternity clinics, who were drinking alcohol, to a 10-min educational cognitive behavior intervention followed by a session supplemented with a self-help manual for reducing alcohol, or to standard clinic care (Reynolds, Coombs, Lowe, Peterson, & Gayoso, 1995). Those receiving the cognitive intervention had a higher quit rate (88%) than those in the standard clinic care group (69%).

3.5   Summary

Preventing AEPs is an important public health issue. Although most women are aware that developmental consequences are linked to very heavy drinking during pregnancy, there is far less awareness that drinking low to moderate amounts of alcohol is associated with developmental disabilities. This, coupled with the fact that almost half of all pregnancies are not planned, as well as high numbers of women reporting that they have not used birth control methods effectively, leaves many women unintentionally at risk of an AEP.

To address these problems, several well-designed and controlled CHOICES interventions were recently developed, evaluated, and found to be successful. All preconception interventions have shown consistent effects, with improvements in both contraception and drinking practices. They also demonstrate the need to view AEP prevention through two lenses: promoting effective, consistent contraception, and promoting reduced risk drinking.

What all of the CHOICES interventions have in common is the use of a MI counseling style that includes counseling components that have their history in social learning theory and cognitive behavior therapy. They all use procedures that recognize that at-risk women may be ambivalent about changing, and therefore confrontational approaches should be avoided. All six interventions studied were brief and ranged from one to five sessions. Some studies involved face-to-face sessions with a therapist, some conducted sessions by phone, and some disseminated the information about avoiding an AEP using brochures that were motivational in nature and sent out by regular mail. Some included a family planning visit and others did not.

Dissemination is an important concept. From a health care systems perspective, it is important to recognize that some women who received a minimal CHOICES intervention showed substantial changes in drinking even when they were assigned to a control group. In the studies reviewed earlier, educational materials appear to have been nearly as effective in preventing an AEP as more structured clinical interventions. In addition, several studies now suggest that change might be mediated by assessments administered to participants. Taken together, these findings suggest that an assessment paired with a minimal educational intervention (e.g., informational pamphlet) may lead some women to take actions to avoid an AEP. That is, once their awareness of their own drinking patterns and contraception is raised, they may become motivated to act to prevent becoming pregnant or appreciate the importance

Because AEPs are preventable, their permanent consequences can be avoided!

Help us prevent AEP: We are asking everyone reading this book to talk with their patients about how to prevent an AEP

of having healthy babies if they should become pregnant. This suggests that a stepped-care model would be a reasonable approach to use to provide treatment, where at-risk women are first presented with a minimal intervention and then followed up, with more intensive interventions being reserved for those who do not respond to a minimal intervention (Sobell & Sobell 2000). Because AEPs can be prevented and because their consequences are permanent, dedicated efforts to prevent AEPs should be a national health priority.

4

Treatment: Dissemination Efforts for Avoiding Alcohol-Exposed Pregnancies

4.1   Knowledge About AEP and FASD Among Practitioners and the Public

As discussed in Chapter 1, as a science, the field of FASD is relatively new. Although much has been learned about the risks associated with prenatal alcohol exposure since the first published study (Jones et al., 1973), the problem of AEPs is substantial, as demonstrated by the high number of unplanned pregnancies and the high percentage of women who are drinking at risky levels.

Over the past decade, a series of well-controlled prevention studies funded by the CDC has specifically targeted women of reproductive age who are at risk of an AEP. A hallmark of these studies is that they provided choices to women who are at risk of an AEP – that is, women were told that they could choose which of two target behaviors (i.e., risky drinking or ineffective or no contraception) they wanted to change, or choose to change both. Collectively, the six studies have solidly demonstrated that brief to minimal interventions (e.g., brochures) can successfully reduce the risks of AEP.

Although knowledge of the risks of drinking during pregnancy has gained attention and momentum, practitioners' awareness lags behind the evidence. The three examples below suggest that many health and mental health care practitioners are greatly in need of information about (a) FASD, (b) preventing AEPs, and (c) assessment, screening, and referral resources.

The first example, a review of 81 obstetrics textbooks used in medical schools from 1970 through 2000 (Loop & Nettleman, 2002), examined what the textbooks recommended in relation to maternal drinking during pregnancy. The study found that only 17% of the texts contained a recommendation advising pregnant women not to drink when pregnant. When the review was narrowed to textbooks from 1991 to 2000, only 24% made such a recommendation. In contrast, 52% of texts published during that period contained a sentence condoning drinking at some level, and the remaining 24% had no recommendations.

The second example is a survey of Fellows of the American College of Obstetricians and Gynecologists (ACOG) who were asked about their knowledge, opinions, and practices regarding their patients' use of alcohol (Anderson et al., 2010). Considering that these physicians specialize in women's reproductive issues and pregnancies, one might expect that they would have known about the risks of an AEP. However, only 66% of the 369 physicians surveyed indicated that occasional alcohol consumption is not safe for pregnant women. The percentage was much lower when they were asked about the effects of alcohol on fetal development. While 47% of the obstetricians/gynecologists surveyed felt they had a clear understanding, 53% said they did not. Although more than three quarters (82%) reported that they asked all their pregnant patients about their alcohol use at the initial visit, only 11% reported asking these same women about their drinking at a subsequent visit. Three quarters (78%) also said they advised their pregnant patients to not drink when pregnant. Interestingly, older physicians reported feeling less prepared than their younger colleagues in terms of screening for hazardous or risky drinking. The most common issues that affected these physicians' decision to screen for alcohol were "patient denial or resistance to treatment" (Anderson et al., 2010, p. 114), and concern about lacking "referral resources for patients with alcohol problems" (p. 114). Lastly, when asked if they had used currently available resources (e.g., ACOG's Fetal Alcohol Spectrum Disorder Prevention Tool Kit or the NIAAA's *Clinician's Guide*), most said that they were not aware of such resources (see Appendix 2 for links to these and other guides and resources that are currently available for free to practitioners).

The third example, a large random survey of members of the American Psychological Association (Wedding et al., 2007), found considerable gaps in psychologists' knowledge about AEPs and the diagnosis, treatment, and prevention of FASD. For example, the prevalence of FAS was underestimated: 11% felt occasional use of alcohol during pregnancy would not harm the fetus, and most could not identify the classic dysmorphia associated with FAS. Further, when asked how prepared they were to identify children with FASD, 65% said they felt they were "very to somewhat unprepared," whereas only 4% felt "very prepared." To their credit, 85% of the psychologists reported a desire to learn more about FASD (e.g., continuing education, materials on the Internet, or self-study materials).

In addition to the groups in the three examples discussed above, the general population also lacks knowledge and/or an appreciation of the risks associated with an AEP. This lack of knowledge is especially troubling for two groups of women: (a) those who become pregnant and continue to drink, and (b) those who are not planning to become pregnant, but who are not contracepting effectively and are drinking at levels that would place their unborn child at risk of an AEP. Unfortunately, some pregnant women believe that "light" drinking late in their pregnancy poses no risk (Mengel, Searight, & Cook, 2006) despite widespread information to the contrary (e.g., warning labels, signs in drinking bars).

4.2   Developing Programs for Preventing AEPs

While the study by Wedding et al. (2007) found large deficits in psychologists' knowledge about the diagnosis, treatment, and prevention of these problems, it is reasonable to think that these deficits probably extend to other health and mental health practitioners (e.g., nurses, physicians, social workers, physician assistants, pharmacists, psychiatrists). Wedding and colleagues suggested that if psychologists are to prevent AEPs and to better identify and treat children with FASD, they need "additional educational resources in FASD prevention, recognition, diagnosis, and treatment" (Wedding et al. 2007, p. 212). These authors also suggested that if practitioners "take the time necessary to become informed about screening and prevention of FASD, they can make a genuine contribution to public health and help reduce the number of children exposed to alcohol *in utero* as well as the often devastating consequences associated with this exposure" (p. 212).

4.3   Things Practitioners Can Do To Help Women Prevent an AEP

All practitioners who work with women of reproductive age can play a critical role in preventing AEPs, and their FASD sequelae.

The first thing all practitioners should do is ask a few brief screening questions to determine if a woman is at risk of an AEP. As discussed in Chapter 2, two brief screening questions can determine whether a woman is at risk for an AEP: Question 1, which is about binge drinking, inquires about risky drinking levels: "*During the past year, how often did you have 4 or more alcoholic drinks in a day?*" Question 2 asks about effective methods of birth control: "*Do you always use effective birth control methods when having heterosexual intercourse?*" These two questions identify almost all women in need of further screening. A positive answer to the first question and a negative answer to the second question suggests the need for further screening. For practitioners who want a more detailed assessment, Appendix 5 contains a brief AEP-risk assessment that includes questions on how to properly use common contraceptive methods.

Two questions can identify almost all women who are at risk of an AEP

The second thing all practitioners should do is provide at-risk women with accurate information about how to prevent an AEP (see Appendix 2 for links to brochures that have been used in various CHOICES interventions). Further, practitioners who feel qualified could deliver CHOICES or one of the briefer CHOICES-like interventions (see Chapter 3). For example, they could provide brief advice and hand out one of the CHOICES-like brochures, and if needed, offer a referral for specialty services.

The third thing practitioners can do is to promote effective contraception among sexually active women. In most communities and on the Internet, there are brochures and listings of where women can go to find a local health center to obtain birth control. In settings where it is possible, providers should also consider coordinating their programs to reduce drinking with programs for reproductive health.

4.4   Putting CHOICES Into Practice

As discussed in Chapter 3, there is very strong evidence that brief motivational counseling with nonpregnant, at-risk women of childbearing age reduces the risk of an AEP. Widespread dissemination of CHOICES and CHOICES-like interventions is a priority of the CDC's Division of Birth Defects and Developmental Disabilities. The CDC has made available Project CHOICES intervention resources (detailed below), and they are developing a marketing and dissemination plan for Project CHOICES products and training. As reviewed in Chapter 3, several adaptations of the CHOICES intervention have been developed and evaluated (e.g., fewer sessions, no family planning session, brochures sent by mail with no clinic contact, community health centers and family planning clinics, sexually transmitted disease clinics). Since its early inception, the CHOICES intervention has been extended to several other groups and populations (e.g., Native American women, alcohol rehabilitation programs, college women, Spanish-speaking women). Although CHOICES has not been tested with women younger than 18 years, the following are the CDC's recommendations when using CHOICES with teens: (a) use your program's or agency's guidelines when discussing alcohol use with underage women; (b) all types of birth control may not be available for younger women; (c) sexual relations between underage teens and older boys or men may be a reportable crime in some states, and (d) know your reporting responsibilities, and inform your patients of your requirement to report underage sexual or drinking behavior.

4.4.1   CHOICES' Training Resources

To facilitate dissemination and implementation, the CDC, its contractors, and the original investigators have worked together on the CHOICES intervention (Velasquez et al., 2010) to produce high-quality training materials (available at http://www.cdc.gov/NCBDDD/fasd/freematerials.html). These materials include:

- *Facilitator Guide*: This guide is a resource for trainers that includes slides, handouts, and pretests and posttests for conducting training sessions.
- *Videos:* These five videos are resources for trainers where an actress plays the role of a patient. Actual CHOICES counselors demonstrate the different components of the intervention. A closed-caption version of the videos is being developed and will be available at the same website as the other materials. A reference guide is available that provides a supplement to the videos.
- *Counselor Manual:* The counselor/interventionist manual was designed for use by trainees during CHOICES training courses.
- *Client Workbook:* The client workbook was designed for patients who receive the CHOICES intervention. Trainees can also use it during the training course to become familiar with the CHOICES materials.

4.4.2   Additional Training Considerations

Although the available AEP training materials are very helpful, some agencies and programs might want to consider more intensive training, particularly in terms of practicing the MI skills that are an integral part of all CHOICES sessions.

Before implementing a CHOICES intervention, agencies or programs should consider the appropriateness of the intervention for their target population and program staff (Hutton et al., 2014). To be successful, CHOICES should be acceptable to the program staff, service providers, and patients. We strongly recommend that agencies considering adopting a CHOICES or a CHOICES-like intervention examine whether the CHOICES rationale (i.e., *women who are not pregnant* have the right and responsibility to use effective contraception and to choose if and how much alcohol to drink) fits with their agency's message and mission. For example, in implementing CHOICES at a facility for women who are severely dependent on alcohol, encouraging effective contraception might be the most likely way to prevent an AEP.

The sustainability of CHOICES programming is another important consideration. In an evaluation conducted by Macro International for the CDC, evaluators recommended increasing the sustainability of CHOICES programming by (a) gaining a commitment from high-level administrators, and by developing agency-specific plans to sustain the CHOICES program. Preventing AEPs is one of the most important ways to avoid developmental disabilities. For that reason, all practitioners who work with women of reproductive age should be aware of the risk of AEPs and of the crucial role that health care practitioners can play to minimize these risks to unborn children. Finally, one way to maintain the CHOICES programming in settings where it is not feasible to have multiple sessions is to reduce the number of sessions and provide women with written CHOICES material to supplement the sessions.

4.4.3   Cultural Adaptations of the CHOICES Intervention

In addition to the several successful adaptations that have been made to the original CHOICES intervention (e.g., fewer sessions, no family planning visit, brochures in place of a clinic visit), CHOICES has undergone specific cultural adaptations that have now been successfully evaluated with Native American and Spanish-speaking women. An excellent example of a cultural adaption involves the CDC entering into an Inter-Agency Agreement with the Indian Health Service (IHS) to implement CHOICES in settings serving American Indian and Alaska Native women. The IHS also funded the Oglala Sioux Tribe (OST) to oversee the implementation of CHOICES in several health care settings in South Dakota (CHOICES Training of Trainers, 2013). In these settings, the CHOICES curriculum was adapted to meet specific cultural needs of Native American women (e.g., slowing the intervention pace by reducing session content to allow more internal processing, and selecting images and themes that resonate with Native American women; developing specific AEP risk vignettes for Native American women). The OST is providing CHOICES sessions to Native American women in tribal health centers and in Rapid City (South Dakota) health clinics. The intervention in these settings has reduced self-reported drinking from 17% to 26%, depending on the setting, and reduced no contraceptive use from 29% to 10% (Hanson et al., 2013). The National Organization on Fetal Alcohol Syndrome (NOFAS), a group dedicated to the prevention and increasing awareness of FASD, has recently published a report (NOFAS, 2014a) that provides a detailed implementation plan and resource referral guide that is useful in delivering CHOICES in clinical settings that serve American Indian and Alaska Native women of childbearing age. The PDF for this report can be found at http://www.nofas.org/wp-content/ uploads/2014/08/Implementing-CHOICES-in-Clinical-Settings-that-Serve-American-Indian-and-Alaska-Native-Women-of-Childbearing-Age.pdf. To reach other groups and cultures, CHOICES materials have been translated into Spanish. For instance, AltaMed Corporation, a community health center CHOICES site in Los Angeles, has produced a Spanish translation of the CHOICES client workbook, and the New York City Health and Hospital Corporation family planning clinic site has translated CHOICES screening materials into 13 languages. These may be ordered through the CDC website (http://www.cdc.gov/ncbddd/fasd/index.html). AltaMed has also developed extensive outreach efforts in the Los Angeles area (e.g., parent programs in schools, community health fairs, treatment centers) to encourage Latina women to come to clinics to be screened for the CHOICES intervention. Project Healthy CHOICES materials were translated and retrotranslated into Spanish and are available through the Healthy Lifestyles Guided Self-Change program website (http://www.nova.edu/gsc).

An encouraging note that demonstrates increased awareness of AEPs is that the first International Conference on Prevention of FASD (Canada, September, 2013) acknowledged new efforts in several countries (e.g., Canada, Ireland, Italy, South Africa) to prevent FASD during preconception as well as when women are pregnant. Although many of the new initiatives presented at this conference used CHOICES concepts, most are so new that there are little or no data available. However, one CHOICES-like program in Canada, Healthy Child Manitoba, which has existed for over a decade, not only targets teens and younger adults in high-risk settings, but also uses online recruitment (http://www.gov.mb.ca/healthychild/fasd/choices.html).

Finally, a RCT of a dual-focused intervention, involving two 5-min physician-conducted CHOICES-like sessions occurring 1 month apart, was conducted in Russia (Balachova et al., 2013). Although there are well-established free OB/GYN health care services for women (e.g., prenatal care, family planning, contraception services) in Russia, the rationale for incorporating CHOICES into their treatment as normal practice (i.e., women typically receive no specific intervention) was to have the physicians learn the MI style in the hope that they could motivate more women to contracept effectively or to reduce their drinking to nonrisky levels. The intervention was evaluated at public women's clinics in two locations, with 10 clinics at each location (i.e., Nizhny Novgorod Region: small rural clinics; St. Petersburg: large urban clinics). Preliminary evaluations indicate that there was a significant reduction in the overall AEP risk at the 12-month follow-up.

4.4.4   Future Considerations

The availability of free materials and a regionally diverse cohort of CHOICES trainers, and modifications to the intervention and settings discussed in Chapter 3 and this chapter, show that the dissemination of CHOICES and CHOICES-like interventions has been successful, particularly in the United States, Canada, and Russia. The widespread dissemination of the CHOICES interventions in a short period of time, coupled with their impressive success rates, suggests the dissemination and adoption of CHOICES will continue to increase. As with all evidence-based treatments, one final caveat for practitioners is that it is important to maintain fidelity with the CHOICES protocol. Thus, programs and practitioners interested in implementing or adopting CHOICES are encouraged to tailor the intervention to their target populations, and to seek training and consultation as needed.

4.5   Impact of CHOICES Dissemination on Public Policy

The impact of CHOICES has already begun to influence public policy at the state level in the United States. For example, the Texas Office for the Prevention of Developmental Disabilities (TOPDD), a highly influential state agency, led efforts for the integration of CHOICES into community substance abuse and mental health agencies. According to the TOPDD, the success of CHOICES fueled key stakeholders' interest in FASD, which resulted in the development of a groundbreaking statewide plan on FASD. Consequently, Texas law now requires that all individuals (male and female) who are served by a state-funded addiction treatment facility must receive education in FASD. TOPDD's executive director's comments reflect how widespread this influence could be:

> This is the tip of the iceberg. There are a host of policies and rule changes that are being targeted. Most importantly, the groundswell of interest in FASD has increased the demand for professional training and education tremendously. It is important to consider that the partners of community based entities such as treatment and recovery agencies include influential constituencies such as the court systems. Implementing CHOICES has had a tremendous impact on women and their families. In addition, it has the potential of a ripple effect that reaches beyond the individuals who are served directly. (J. Sharkis, personal communication, July 17, 2014)

While the CHOICES results have been impressive, further strategic and concerted efforts at all state levels are needed. In this regard, monitoring of the costs and benefits of the many CHOICES interventions can be used to inform potential providers and policymakers.

Finally, it is important to view the prevention of AEPs from both a systemic and public health perspective. Considering this dual approach, a variety of services and venues can be involved to maximize coverage and efficiency. The broadest and least intensive layer of such an approach involves increasing public knowledge and awareness of FASD, particularly of AEP. For many women, as demonstrated by the two CHOICES-like interventions that use brochures, a simple awareness of the issues (e.g., informational brochures widely available in public and health care settings) appears to be sufficient to prompt them to make better-informed decisions about how to avoid an AEP.

Implementing screening programs in different settings (e.g., college campuses, primary care centers, OB/GYN clinics, family planning programs) will also encourage some women to enact changes. In almost all of the CHOICES and CHOICES-like studies, women in the control conditions who received either standard care or very little guidance about one or both target behaviors changed their drinking, contraceptive practices, or both. It seems possible that just knowing that they have been identified as at risk (e.g., by agreeing to an informed consent for the study or by completing assessment materials) may have led them to reflect on their risky behavior(s) and to take action to avoid an AEP.

4.6   CHOICES-Like Interventions in Colleges and Universities: An Easy, Effective, and Essential Dissemination Effort

In two of the five CHOICES-like interventions, all or close to half of all participants were college students (Ceperich & Ingersoll, 2011; Project BALANCE; Sobell et al., 2015; Sobell, Sobell, Johnson, & Bolton, 2007; Project Healthy Choices, July). For both studies, the interventions for both the experimental and control groups were brief. It is interesting to note that the CHOICES-like interventions (experimental group) for the college students in both studies had the highest overall reduced risk of an AEP (i.e., 80% and 79%, respectively) of any CHOICES study discussed in Chapter 3, including the original CHOICES study, which had an impressive 69% risk reduction rate. There is another notable finding in the two CHOICES studies with students: As compared with CHOICES studies that did not involve students, a much larger percentage of college students chose to contracept effectively as opposed to changing their alcohol use to nonrisky levels (although some did both). Thus, it appears the very high success rates in these two studies with women in college were more a result of their changing their birth control methods than of changing their drinking. Further, the comparable figures for each study's control group (i.e., non-CHOICES intervention) were similarly high (i.e., BALANCE = 65%; Healthy CHOICES = 66%). Both studies' control groups used a single informational brochure (BALANCE used one on women's health; Healthy CHOICES used the CDC's FAS pamphlet). This may indicate that, at least with college students, even minimal information – when derived from the CHOICES intervention – is associated with behavior change to prevent an AEP.

CHOICES-like interventions with college students are brief, very inexpensive and effective, and thus warrant integration into student health services on all campuses

One appealing interpretation of the positive findings for college students is that upon learning they were at risk of an "unintended" or "unwanted" pregnancy, many immediately adopted effective contraceptive practices or reduced their drinking to nonrisky levels or both. Presumably, this would occur because becoming pregnant was not consistent with their immediate plans to finish college or have a career. The fact that the two CHOICES-like interventions with college students were brief, minimally intrusive, very inexpensive, and very effective warrants their integration into student health services on all college and university campuses.

Another way to look at the positive results from the CHOICES interventions might be from a decisional balance perspective, given that the motivational strategy of decisional balancing is a fundamental part of most of the CHOICES interventions. With regard to college students, for instance, it may be that reading the intervention materials and weighing the pros and cons of changing their contraceptive and alcohol use behaviors moved them toward deciding that the negative consequences (i.e., unwanted or unplanned child at the current time) tipped the scales in favor of changing their behavior to avoid an AEP.

4.7   Conclusion

The CHOICES interventions are unique in that they allow women to select the health behavior(s) they want to change. The very high rates of change observed across all of the CHOICES and CHOICES-like studies reflects what Albert Bandura suggested years ago – that when people are given choice in setting their goals, they are likely to have better outcomes (Bandura, 1997). The attractiveness of a CHOICES intervention is that it allows women and practitioners to embrace multiple pathways to change to prevent an AEP.

CHOICES interventions are unique: They allow women to select the behavior(s) they want to change

5

Case Vignette

In this case vignette, a portion of a CHOICES session is simulated. Essential clinical skills called motivational interviewing (MI) are highlighted. The reason for using MI strategies is to emphasize a woman's autonomy and *CHOICE* in making decisions about her health and behavior change. In using MI skills, the practitioner asks open-ended questions, uses reflective listening, affirms, and summarizes the woman's comments in an effort to elicit and reinforce her reasons for change. The session should be collaborative, as the practitioner should not be acting like the "expert" but rather eliciting the woman's own ideas about change. This is as opposed to telling, informing, or lecturing her about the need to change. In addition, the practitioner delivers personalized feedback in a nonjudgmental manner. The information provided is preceded by assessing the woman's interest and asking her permission to provide feedback about her health and preventing AEPs. (After some of the practitioner's statements in the following, there is a description of the MI strategy or technique used, in brackets and set in boldface type.)

The Emphasis in a CHOICES Intervention is on Allowing Women to Choose to Change Either of Two Behaviors: Reduce Her Alcohol Use or Contracept Effectively

Kristen is a 23-year-old woman who recently got married.
Practitioner: Kristen, I know you reported you drink alcohol on occasion and that you mentioned that you are thinking of having a family down the road. Would you mind if we talk about what we call an alcohol-exposed pregnancy?
Client: Sure, that's fine.
Practitioner: When a woman drinks alcohol when she is pregnant, the baby is also exposed to alcohol and that can affect the unborn child's development. Although we do not know the exact amount of alcohol it takes to have an effect on a baby, we do know that in some cases even small amounts of alcohol can sometimes be harmful. Another thing to think about is that women can be many weeks into their pregnancy before they even know they are pregnant. What are your thoughts about what I have said? **[Provision of information; Asking open-ended question]**
Client: I know that pregnant women shouldn't drink a lot, but I never thought about the fact that someone might drink and harm a baby even before they know they're pregnant.
Practitioner: It's something to think about. **[Reflection]**
Client: Definitely, and when I try to become pregnant, I'll keep that in mind.

Practitioner: In CHOICES, we talk with women about preventing an alcohol-exposed pregnancy in two ways. One way is to use birth control effectively. The reason we do this is that sometimes women who are using a method of birth control do not use it as intended, such as missing a pill and not using a backup method like a condom. Therefore, what we do is explore the options you have for selecting a method of birth control. How does that sound?

Client: Fine.

Practitioner: Although alcohol use is common for many women, about half of all pregnancies are not planned. Therefore, the second way that we discuss avoiding an alcohol-exposed pregnancy is to reduce your drinking to below risky levels. Of course, we also advise not drinking if you become pregnant. I have given you a lot of information. What has stood out for you?

Client: Well, lots of things, but when you said 50% of pregnancies are unplanned, that sounds high. I wouldn't want to be partying on a weekend and later find out I was pregnant. Who wants a messed-up kid?

Practitioner: Kristen, we can take a look at your drinking over the past few months and give you information you can think about in terms of avoiding risky drinking. The very best protection against an alcohol-exposed pregnancy for all women who are not pregnant is to avoid risky drinking and to use birth control effectively. Any questions so far? Which of the two options would you like to chat about first – changing your alcohol use or making sure your contraception use is effective, or both? **[Provision of information; Asking open-ended questions; Providing choice]**

Client: Let's talk about drinking first. Do women really drink that much? I mean I know many of my friends and I might on occasion have a few too many when celebrating, but I don't drink that much in general. However, I would like some information on birth control pills and what to do if you miss one.

Practitioner: Okay, as you requested let's start with your drinking. **[Reflection; Discussion with first focus in the area requested by the client]**

Client: Sounds good to me.

Note: The woman chose to talk about her drinking first and that is her choice. Remember, the relationship is viewed as collaborative and emphasizes the person's autonomy. Consequently, the focus of the discussion will start with the woman's alcohol use. Another patient, however, could decide to discuss birth control methods first and that would be fine, too. What the research literature shows is that when people are given choice they are not only happier and more satisfied, but on a group basis, choice usually results in better outcomes (Bandura, 2001).

Delivering Personalized Feedback: The information should always be delivered in a conversational, nonjudgmental manner. When delivering information and feedback, it is important to first ask the person's permission. For example, a practitioner could say, "Do you remember when I asked you some questions about your alcohol use? Well, I took that information and prepared some information for you."

Throughout the feedback process, frequently invite the person to participate in the dialogue by asking about her thoughts or reactions. This also creates opportunities for eliciting "change talk" (i.e., statements such as client-generated reasons or desires to change). Examples of such "invitations" include, "What do you think about this information?" or "It looks like you are surprised by what you see on the graphs."

It is also important to pay attention to nonverbal behavior (e.g., furrowing of the eyebrows, a sigh, a smile, or tears). Use reflective listening to respond to both verbal and nonverbal language. For example, "I get the sense by your frown that this information surprises you," or "I am sensing that this is a little hard to hear right now."

At the end of the session, summarize significant elements of the session. You can also ask the woman what one or two things about the session stood out for her. You will want to highlight any change talk that you have heard that includes expressions of desire or commitment to change.

Practitioner: Let's take a few minutes to go over some of the feedback based on your answers to the questions about your alcohol use. From what you told us, your current drinking level, as compared with other women of your age, falls into the risky drinking level. It shows that you are drinking more than 50% of the women your age group do. You look surprised. **[Implicit asking consent to share information; Provision of information followed by open-ended question]**

Client: Well, most of my friends drink much more than me. Pretty surprising.

Practitioner: That's not an unusual response; we hear that from many young women. **[Normalizing]** You also told us that while you used birth control pills, you have missed several days in a row. What did we go over earlier about that?

Client: It means that I could get pregnant, and I don't need that right now.

Practitioner: It sounds like that worries you a bit. **[Reflection]**

Client: I guess. (sigh)

Practitioner: What concerns you the most?

Client: That my drinking seems high. I don't get that.

Practitioner: Would it be okay if we talk about some of the problems that can be associated with drinking at that level? **[Asking permission]**

Client: (nods)

Discussing Importance, Confidence, and Readiness to Change Behavior(s)

Practitioner: On a scale from 0 to 10, where 0 is not important at all and 10 is being very important, how important is it for you RIGHT NOW to drink below risk levels?

(**Note:** You might have to remind the patient of what constitutes risky drinking.)

Client: Well, about a 5.

Practitioner: A 5. So it sounds like it is important, but so are many other things in your life. **[Reflection of what the number means]** Why did you pick a 5 and not a 2? **[Open-ended question to elicit change talk]**

Client: Well, it is important, but I have a lot going on in my life.

Practitioner: Well, that's understandable. What would it take for you to move from a 5 to 7? **[Open-ended question to elicit more change talk]**

Client: Well, I sometimes get in arguments with my boyfriend when I have had some drinks, and that might not happen if I cut down a little. I just have a lot of stress right now with my boyfriend, and my work is driving me crazy. Sometimes drinking helps relieve the stress, so if my stress was lower, I might be able to reduce my drinking more.

Practitioner: So, what I hear you saying is that, on the one hand, drinking helps relieve your stress, and on the other hand, you have some concerns about how drinking affects your relationship with your boyfriend. You are also thinking about how it might affect your health and some of the new information we just discussed. **[Summary reflection of change talk]**

Client: (nods)

Practitioner: Now, if you don't mind, let's look at your confidence. On a scale from 0 to 10, where 0 is not at all confident and 10 is very confident, how confident are you RIGHT NOW that you can maintain your drinking at below risky levels?

Client: A 3.

Practitioner: So about a 3, which suggests you are not that confident right now that you can engage in low-risk drinking. **[Reflection]** What would it take for your confidence to increase a bit, to move from a 3 to a 5? **[Open-ended question to elicit change talk]**

Client: I guess I would have to have several successful times of only having an occasional drink after dinner. That might be hard, but I will try it next week.

Practitioner: If you were able to successfully reduce your drinking, how would you feel about that? **[Asking the person to give voice to the change process vs. saying it is great]**

Client: It would be a big change for me.

Practitioner: Yes, a big difference for you than in the past. **[Practitioner affirms the woman's change talk after the change talk is elicited]**

6

Further Reading

Floyd, R. L., Sobell, M. B., Velasquez, M. M., Ingersoll, K., Nettleman, M., Sobell, L. C.; Project CHOICES Efficacy Study Group. (2007). Preventing alcohol-exposed pregnancies: A randomized controlled trial. *American Journal of Preventive Medicine, 32*(1), 1–10.

This is the main outcomes paper from the CHOICES efficacy trial. It describes the original CHOICES intervention (four manual-guided MI sessions coupled with one contraceptive counseling visit). Results of the efficacy trial are presented and followed by a discussion of the promise of brief motivational interventions in reducing risk of AEPs in high-risk settings.

Miller, W. R., & Rollnick, S. (2013). *Motivational interviewing: Preparing people for change* (3rd ed.). New York, NY: Guilford Press.

This is the latest edition of a book on motivational interviewing written by MI pioneers William Miller and Stephen Rollnick. The book reflects recent advances in MI and provides vignettes and interview examples to guide readers who are learning to use this approach.

Project CHOICES Research Group. (2002). Alcohol-exposed pregnancy: Characteristics associated with risk. *American Journal of Preventive Medicine, 23*(3), 166–173.

This manuscript describes the CHOICES epidemiological survey that was administered to 2,672 women of childbearing age in six diverse settings, These settings included an urban jail, a drug/alcohol treatment facility, a gynecology clinic, two primary care clinics, and respondents to a media solicitation. This paper provides a useful discussion of the characteristics associated with AEP risk among women in these settings.

Project CHOICES Intervention Research Group. (2003). Reducing the risk of alcohol-exposed pregnancies: A study of a motivational intervention in community settings. *Pediatrics 111*(5), 1131–1135.

This manuscript summarizes the outcomes of the CHOICES feasibility trial, a study that tested the feasibility and impact of the original CHOICES intervention in six high-risk settings (an urban jail, a drug/alcohol treatment facility, a gynecology clinic, two primary care clinics, and a media solicitation). Results were consistent across settings and suggested that the CHOICES intervention can decrease risk of AEP.

Substance Abuse and Mental Health Services Administration. (2014). *Addressing fetal alcohol spectrum disorders (FASD)*. Treatment Improvement Protocol (TIP) Series 58. (HHS Publication No. [SMA] 13-4803). Rockville, MD: Author.

This comprehensive resource book provides an introduction to FASD and reviews various alcohol screening tools and interventions that can be used to identify women at risk for AEP. It also provides information on how to identify and treat individuals with FASD and suggests resources for them and their families. (This publication may be ordered from SAMHSA's publications Web page at http://store.samhsa.gov/home or by calling +1 877 726-4727).

Velasquez, M. M., Ingersoll, K. S., Sobell, M. B., Floyd, R. L., Sobell, L. C., & von Sternberg, K. (2010). A dual-focus motivational intervention to reduce the risk of alcohol-exposed pregnancy. *Cognitive and Behavioral Practice, 17*(2), 203–212.
This manuscript describes each of the four CHOICES intervention sessions in detail, offering useful tips for counselors. It also details the development of the CHOICES intervention, study protocol, and treatment manual, along with the approach used to select, train, supervise, and monitor the study counselors to assure intervention fidelity.

7

References

Abel, E. L. (1990). *Fetal alcohol syndrome*. Oradell, NJ: Medical Economics Press.

Alati, R., Kinner, S. A., Hayatbakhsh, M. R., Mamun, A. A., Najman, J. M., & Williams, G. M. (2008). Pathways to ecstasy use in young adults: Anxiety, depression or behavioural deviance? *Drug and Alcohol Dependence, 92*(1), 108–115. http://doi.org/10.1016/j.drugalcdep.2007.07.007

American Psychiatric Association. (2013). *Diagnostic and statistical manual of mental disorders (5th ed.)*. Washington, DC: Author.

Anderson, B. L., Dang, E. P., Floyd, R. L., Sokol, R., Mahoney, J., & Schulkin, J. (2010). Knowledge, opinions, and practice patterns of obstetrician-gynecologists regarding their patients' use of alcohol. *Journal of Addiction Medicine, 4*(2), 114–121. http://doi.org/10.1097/ADM.0b013e3181b95015

Astley, S. J. (2011). Diagnosing fetal alcohol spectrum disorders (FASD). In S. A. Adubato & D. E. Cohen (Eds.), *Prenatal alcohol use and fetal alcohol spectrum disorders: Diagnosis, assessment and new directions in research and multimodal treatment* (pp. 3–29). Oak Park, IL: Bentham eBooks.

Astley, S. J., & Clarren, S. K. (2000). Diagnosing the full spectrum of fetal alcohol-exposed individuals: Introducing the 4-digit diagnostic code. *Alcohol and Alcoholism, 35*(4), 400–410. http://doi.org/10.1093/alcalc/35.4.400

Balachova, T., Bonner, B., Chaffin, M., Bard, D., Isurina, G., Tsvetkova, L., & Volkova, E. (2012). Women's alcohol consumption and risk for alcohol-exposed pregnancies in Russia. *Addiction (Abingdon, England), 107*(1), 109–117. http://doi.org/10.1111/j.1360-0443.2011.03569.x

Balachova, T., Bonner, B., Chaffin, M., Isurina, G., Tsvetkova, L., Volkova, E., & Agrawal, S. (2013). Dual-focused brief physician intervention to reduce the risk for alcohol-exposed pregnancies: A randomized controlled trial. *Alcoholism-Clinical and Experimental Research, 37*, 50A–50A.

Balachova, T. N., Sobell, L. C., Agrawal, S., Isurina, G., Tsvetkova, L., Volkova, E., & Bohora, S.B. (in press). Using a single binge-drinking question to identify Russian women at risk for an alcohol-exposed pregnancy. *Addictive Behaviors.*

Bandura, A. (1997). *Self-efficacy: The exercise of self-control*. Gordonsville, VA: WH Freeman & Co.

Bandura, A. (2001). Social cognitive theory: An agentic perspective. *Annual Review of Psychology, 52*(1), 1–26. http://doi.org/10.1146/annurev.psych.52.1.1

Bertrand, J., & Dang, E. P. (2012). Fetal alcohol spectrum disorders: Review of teratogenicity, diagnosis and treatment issues. In D. Hollar (Ed.), *Handbook of children with special health care needs* (pp. 231–258). New York, NY: Springer.

Bertrand, J., Floyd, R. L., & Weber, M. K. (2005). Guidelines for identifying and referring persons with Fetal Alcohol Syndrome. *Mortality and Morbidity Weekly Report (RR 11), 54*, 1–14.

Bertrand, J., Floyd, R. L., Weber, M. K., O'Connor, M., Riley, E. P, Johnson, K. A., & Cohen, D. E. (2004). *Fetal alcohol syndrome: Guidelines for referral and diagnosis*. Atlanta, GA: Centers for Disease Control and Prevention. Retrieved from http://www.cdc.gov/ncbddd/fasd/documents/FAS_guidelines_accessible.pdf

Borsari, B., & Carey, K. B. (2000). Effects of a brief motivational intervention with college student drinkers. *Journal of Consulting and Clinical Psychology, 68*(4), 728–733. http://doi.org/10.1037/0022-006X.68.4.728

Calhoun, F. J. (2011). Foreword. In S. A. Adubato & D. E. Cohen (Eds.), *Prenatal alcohol use and fetal alcohol spectrum disorders: Diagnosis, assessment and new directions in research and multimodal treatment* (pp. i–ii). Bentham eBooks.

Cannon, M. J., Guo, J., Denny, C. H., Green, P. P., Miracle, H., Sniezek, J. E., & Floyd, R. L. (2014). Prevalence and characteristics of women at risk for an alcohol-exposed pregnancy (AEP) in the United States: Estimates from the National Survey of Family Growth. *Maternal and Child Health Journal, 34*(1), 1–7. http://doi.org/10.1007/s10995-014-1563-3

Carey, K., Carey, M., Maisto, S., & Henson, J. (2006). Brief motivational interventions for heavy college drinkers: A randomized controlled trial. *Journal of Consulting and Clinical Psychology, 74*(5), 943–954. http://doi.org/10.1037/0022-006X.74.5.943

Caudill, M. A. (2010). Pre- and postnatal health: Evidence of increased choline needs. *Journal of the American Dietetic Association, 110*(8), 1198–1206. http://doi.org/10.1016/j.jada.2010.05.009

Centers for Disease Control and Prevention, in coordination with National Task Force on Fetal Alcohol Syndrome and Fetal Alcohol Effect. (2004). *Fetal alcohol syndrome: Guidelines for referral and diagnosis.* Retrieved from http://www.cdc.gov/ncbddd/fasd/documents/FAS_guidelines_accessible.pdf

Centers for Disease Control and Prevention. (2009). Alcohol use among pregnant and non-pregnant women of childbearing age – United States, 1991–2005. *Mortality and Morbidity Weekly Report, 58*(19), 529–532. Retrieved from http://www.cdc.gov/mmwr/mmwr/.

Centers for Disease Control and Prevention. (2012). Alcohol use and binge drinking among women of childbearing age: United States, 2006–2010. *Morbidity and Mortality Weekly Report, 61*(28), 4876–4892.

Centers for Disease Control and Prevention. (2013, February 12). *Unintended pregnancy prevention.* Retrieved from http://www.cdc.gov/reproductivehealth/unintendedpregnancy

Centers for Disease Control and Prevention. (2014). *Facts about FASDs.* Retrieved from http://www.cdc.gov/ncbddd/fasd/facts.html

Ceperich, S. D., & Ingersoll, K. S. (2011). Motivational interviewing + feedback intervention to reduce alcohol-exposed pregnancy risk among college binge drinkers: Determinants and patterns of response. *Journal of Behavioral Medicine, 34*, 381–395. http://doi.org/10.1007/s10865-010-9308-2

Chang, G., Wilkins-Haug, L., Berman, S., & Goetz, M. A. (1999). Brief intervention for alcohol use in pregnancy: A randomized trial. *Addiction, 94*(10), 1499–1508. http://doi.org/10.1046/j.1360-0443.1999.941014996.x

CHOICES Training of Trainers. (2013). *CHOICES pre-work booklet: For CHOICES training of trainers.* Unpublished manuscript.

Chudley, A. E., Conry, J., Cook, J. L., Loock, C., Rosales, T., & LeBlanc, N. (2005). Fetal alcohol spectrum disorder: Canadian guidelines for diagnosis. *Canadian Medical Association Journal, 172*(Suppl 5), S1–S21. http://doi.org/10.1503/cmaj.1040302

Clifford, P. R., Maisto, S. A., & Davis, C. M. (2007). Alcohol treatment research assessment exposure subject reactivity effects: Part I. Alcohol use and related consequences. *Journal of Studies on Alcohol and Drugs, 68*(4), 519–528.

Collaborative Initiative on Fetal Alcohol Spectrum Disorders. (2012). *Fetal Alcohol Spectrum Disorders: A series of slides generated for education on current FASD research.* Retrieved from http://cifasd.org/education

Cyr, M. G., & Wartman, S. A. (1990). Screening for alcoholism. *Journal of General Internal Medicine, 5*(4), 379–380. http://doi.org/10.1007/BF02600412

Dawson, D. A. (2000). U.S. low-risk drinking guidelines: An examination of four alternatives. *Alcoholism, Clinical and Experimental Research, 24*(12), 1820–1829. http://doi.org/10.1111/j.1530-0277.2000.tb01986.x

Dawson, D. A., Grant, B. F., & Stinson, F. S. (2005). The AUDIT-C: Screening for alcohol use disorders and risk drinking in the presence of other psychiatric disorders. *Comprehensive Psychiatry, 46*(6), 405–416. http://doi.org/10.1016/j.comppsych.2005.01.006

Dawson, D. A., Smith, S. M., Saha, T. D., Rubinsky, A. D., & Grant, B. F. (2012). Comparative performance of the AUDIT-C in screening for DSM-IV and DSM-5 alcohol use disorders. *Drug and Alcohol Dependence, 126*(3), 384–388. http://doi.org/10.1016/j.drugalcdep.2012.05.029

Dum, M., Sobell, L. C., Sobell, M. B., Heinecke, N., Voluse, A., & Johnson, K. (2009). A quick drinking screen for identifying women at risk for an alcohol-exposed pregnancy. *Addictive Behaviors, 34*(9), 714–716. http://doi.org/10.1016/j.addbeh.2009.04.001

Epstein, E. E., Drapkin, M. L., Yusko, D. A., Cook, S. M., McCrady, B. S., & Jensen, N. K. (2005). Is alcohol assessment therapeutic? Pretreatment change in drinking among alcohol-dependent women. *Journal of Studies on Alcohol and Drugs, 66*(3), 369–378.

Falgreen Erickson, H. L., Mortensen, E. L., Kilburn, T., Underbjerg, M., Bertrand, J., Støvring, H., & Kesmodel, U. S. (2012). The effects of low to moderate prenatal alcohol exposure in early pregnancy on IQ in 5-year-old children. *BJOG: An International Journal of Obstetrics & Gynaecology, 119*(10), 1191–1200. http://doi.org/10.1111/j.1471-0528.2012.03394.x

FASCETS. (2010). *Understanding FASD (Fetal Alcohol Spectrum Disorders)*. Retrieved from http://www.fascets.org/info.html

Finer, L. B., & Henshaw, S. K. (2006). Disparities in rates of unintended pregnancy in the United States, 1994 and 2001. *Perspectives on Sexual and Reproductive Health, 38*(2), 90–96. http://doi.org/10.1363/3809006

Flak, A. L., Su, S., Bertrand, J., Denny, C. H., Kesmodel, U. S., & Cogswell, M. E. (2014). The association of mild, moderate, and binge prenatal alcohol exposure and child neuropsychological outcomes: A meta-analysis. *Alcoholism, Clinical and Experimental Research, 38*(1), 214–226. http://doi.org/10.1111/acer.12214

Floyd, R. L., Sobell, M. B., Velasquez, M. M., Ingersoll, K., Nettleman, M., Sobell, L. C.; Project CHOICES Efficacy Study Group. (2007). Preventing alcohol-exposed pregnancies: A randomized controlled trial. *American Journal of Preventive Medicine, 32*(1), 1–10. http://doi.org/10.1016/j.amepre.2006.08.028

Handmaker, N. S., Miller, W. R., & Manicke, M. (1999). Findings of a pilot study of motivational interviewing with pregnant drinkers. *Journal of Studies on Alcohol and Drugs, 60*(2), 285–290. Retrieved from http://www.jsad.com/

Hanson, J. D., Miller, A. L., Winberg, A., & Elliott, A. J. (2013). Prevention of alcohol-exposed pregnancies among nonpregnant American Indian women. *American Journal of Health Promotion, 27*(3, Suppl): S66–73. http://doi.org/ 10.4278/ajhp.120113-QUAN-2

Henshaw, S. K. (1998). Unintended pregnancy in the United States. *Family Planning Perspectives, 24–29*, 24–46.

Hoyme, H. E., May, P. A., Kalberg, W. O., Kodituwakku, P., Gossage, J. P., Trujillo, P. M., & Robinson, L. K. (2005). A practical clinical approach to diagnosis of fetal alcohol spectrum disorders: Clarification of the 1996 Institute of Medicine criteria. *Pediatrics, 115*(1), 39–47. http://doi.org/10.1542/peds.2005-0702

Hutton, H. E., Chander, G., Green, P. P., Hutsell, C. A., Weingarten, K., & Peterson, K. L. (2014). A novel integration effort to reduce the risk for alcohol-exposed pregnancy among women attending urban STD clinics. *Public Health Reports, 129*(Suppl 1), 56–62. Retrieved from http://www.publichealthreports.org/issueopen.cfm?articleID=3111

Ingersoll, K. S., Ceperich, S. D., Hettema, J. E., Farrell-Carnahan, L., & Penberthy, J. K. (2013). Preconceptual motivational interviewing interventions to reduce alcohol-exposed pregnancy risk. *Journal of Substance Abuse Treatment, 44*(4), 407–416. http://doi.org/10.1016/j.jsat.2012.10.001

Ingersoll, K. S., Ceperich, S. D., Nettleman, M. D., & Johnson, B. A. (2008). Risk drinking and contraception effectiveness among college women. *Psychology and Health, 23*(8), 965–981. Retrieved from http://www.tandfonline.com/loi/gpsh20#.U86FxPldUeE

Institute of Medicine. (1990). *Broadening the base of treatment for alcohol problems*. Washington, DC: National Academies Press.

Institute of Medicine. (1996). *Fetal Alcohol Syndrome: Diagnosis, epidemiology, prevention, and treatment*. Washington, DC: National Academies Press.

Jacobson, J. L., & Jacobson, S. W. (1999). Drinking moderately and pregnancy. Effects on child development. *Alcohol Research & Health, 23*(1), 25–30.

Johnson, K. E., Sobell, M. B., & Sobell, L. C. (2010). Using one question to identify women at risk for an alcohol-exposed pregnancy. *The Journal of the American Osteopathic Association, 110*(7), 381–384.

Jones, K. L., & Smith, D. W. (1973). Recognition of the Fetal Alcohol Syndrome in early infancy. *The Lancet, 302*(7836), 999–1001. http://doi.org/10.1016/S0140-6736(73)91092-1

Jones, K. L., Smith, D. W., Ulleland, C. N., & Streissguth, A. P. (1973). *Pattern of malformations in offspring of alcoholic mothers, The Lancet, 301*(7815), 1267–1271. http://doi.org/10.1016/S0140-6736(73)91291-9

Jones-Webb, R., McKiver, M., Pirie, P., & Miner, K. (1999). Relationships between physician advice and tobacco and alcohol use during pregnancy. *American Journal of Preventative Medicine, 16*(3), 244–247. http://doi.org/10.1016/S0749-3797(98)00097-X

Jonsson, E., Salmon, A., & Warren, K. R. (2014). The international charter on prevention of fetal alcohol spectrum disorder. *The Lancet Global Health, 2*(3), e135–e137. http://doi.org/10.1016/S2214-109X(13)70173-6

Kaner, E. F., Dickinson, H. O., Beyer, F., Pienaar, E., Schlesinger, C., Campbell, F., & Heather, N. (2009). The effectiveness of brief alcohol interventions in primary care settings: A systematic review. *Drug and Alcohol Review, 28*(3), 301–323. http://doi.org/10.1111/j.1465-3362.2009.00071.x

Keenan, K., Grundy, E., Kenward, M. G., & Leon, D. A. (2014). Women's risk of repeat abortions is strongly associated with alcohol consumption: A longitudinal analysis of a Russian National Panel Study, 1994–2009. *PloS One, 9*(3), e90356. http://doi.org/10.1371/journal.pone.0090356

Kesmodel, U. S., Bertrand, J., Støvring, H., Sharpness, B., Denny, C. H., Mortensen, E., & the Lifestyle During Pregnancy Study Group. (2012). The effect of different alcohol drinking patterns in early to mid pregnancy on the child's intelligence, attention, and executive function. *BJOG: An International Journal of Obstetrics and Gynecology, 119*(10), 1180–1190. http://doi.org/10.1111/j.1471-0528.2012.03393.x

Kesmodel, U. S., Falgreen Erikson, H. L., Underberg, M., Kilburn, T. R., Storing, H., . . . Mortensen, E. L. (2012). The effect of alcohol binge drinking in early pregnancy on general intelligence in children. *BJOG: An International Journal of Obstetrics and Gynaecology, 119*(10), 1222–1231. http://doi.org/10.1111/j.1471-0528.2012.03395.x

Korotitsch, W. J., & Nelson-Gray, R. O. (1999). An overview of self-monitoring research in assessment and treatment. *Psychological Assessment, 11*(4), 415–425. http://doi.org/10.1037/1040-3590.11.4.415

Lange, S., Shield, K., Rehm, J., & Popova, S. (2013). Prevalence of fetal alcohol spectrum disorders in child care settings: A meta-analysis. *Pediatrics, 132*(4), e980–e995. http://doi.org/10.1542/peds.2013-0066

Lemoine, P., Harousseau, H., Borteyni, J., & Menuet, J. (1968). Les enfants des parents alcooliques: Anomalies observees a propos de 127 cas [Children of alcoholic parents: Abnormalities observed in 127 cases]. *Quest Médical, 8*, 476–482.

Loop, K. Q., & Nettleman, M. D. (2002). Obstetrical textbooks: Recommendations about drinking during pregnancy. *American Journal of Preventive Medicine, 23*(2), 136–138. http://doi.org/10.1016/S0749-3797(02)00466-X

Marlatt, G. A., & Witkiewitz, K. (2002). Harm reduction approaches to alcohol use: Health promotion, prevention, and treatment. *Addictive Behaviors, 27*(6), 867–886. http://doi.org/10.1016/S0306-4603(02)00294-0

Martino, S., Carroll, K. M., O'Malley, S. S., & Rounsaville, B. J. (2000). Motivational interviewing with psychiatrically ill substance abusing patients. *American Journal on Addictions, 9*(1), 88–91. http://doi.org/10.1080/10550490050172263

May, P. A., Baete, A., Russo, J., Elliott, A. J., Blankenship, J., Kalberg, W. O., . . . Hoyme, H. E. (2014). Prevalence and characteristics of fetal alcohol spectrum disorders. *Pediatrics, 134*(5), 855–866. http://doi.org/10.1542/peds.2013-3319

May, P. A., Gossage, J. P., Kalberg, W. O., Robinson, L. K., Buckley, D., Manning, M., & Hoyme, H. E. (2009). Prevalence and epidemiologic characteristics of FASD from various research methods with an emphasis on recent in-school studies. *Developmental Disabilities Research Reviews, 15*(3), 176–192. http://doi.org/10.1002/ddrr.68

Mengel, M. B., Searight, H. R., & Cook, K. (2006). Preventing alcohol-exposed pregnancies. *Journal of the American Board of Family Medicine, 19*(5), 494–505. http://doi.org/10.3122/jabfm.19.5.494

Miller, W. R., & Rollnick, S. (2012). *Motivational interviewing: Helping people change* (*3rd ed.*). New York, NY: Guilford Press.

Moos, M-K., Bartholomew, N. E., & Lohr, K. N. (2003). Counseling in the clinical setting to prevent unintended pregnancy: An evidence-based research agenda. *Contraception, 67*(2), 115–132. http://doi.org/10.1016/S0010-7824(02)00472-9

Mosher, W. D., Jones, J., & Abma, J. C. (2012). *Intended and unintended births in the United States: 1982–2010.* (National Health Statistics Reports No. 55). Hyattsville, MD: National Center for Health Statistics. Retrieved from http://www.cdc.gov/nchs/data/nhsr/nhsr055.pdf.

National Institute on Alcohol Abuse and Alcoholism. (2004, Winter). *NIAAAA Newsletter* (NIH Publication No. 04-5346). Bethesda, MD: NIAAA Office of Research Translation and Communications.

National Institute on Alcohol Abuse and Alcoholism. (2005). *Module 10K: Fetal alcohol exposure* [Powerpoint slides]. Bethesda, MD: Author. Retrieved from http://pubs.niaaa.nih.gov/publications/Social/Module10KFetaExposure/Module10K.html

National Institute on Alcohol Abuse and Alcoholism. (2013, July). *Fetal alcohol exposure.* Washington DC: Department of Health and Human Services. Retrieved from http://pubs.niaaa.nih.gov/publications/FASDFactsheet/FASD.pdf

National Organization on Fetal Alcohol Syndrome. (2014a, August). *Implementing CHOICES in clinical settings that serve American Indian and Alaska Native women of childbearing age: Report, implementation plan, and resources.* Washington DC: Department of Health and Human Services. Retrieved from http://www.nofas.org/wp-content/uploads/2014/08/Implementing-CHOICES-in-Clinical-Settings-that-Serve-American-Indian-and-Alaska-Native-Women-of-Childbearing-Age.pdf

National Organization on Fetal Alcohol Syndrome. (2014b). *FAQs.* Retrieved from http://www.nofas.org/faqs/

National Organization on Fetal Alcohol Syndrome Colorado – NOFAS. (2013). *Fetal alcohol spectrum disorders FAQ.* Retrieved from http://nofascolorado.org/fasdfaq.htm

Neighbors, C., Larimer, M. E., & Lewis, M. A. (2004). Targeting misperceptions of descriptive drinking norms: Efficacy of a computer-delivered personalized normative feedback intervention. *Journal of Consulting and Clinical Psychology, 72*(3), 434–447. http://doi.org/10.1037/0022-006X.72.3.434

Nguyen, T., & Thomas, J. D. (2011). Fetal alcohol spectrum disorders and nutrition. In M. J. O'Connor (Topic Ed.), R. E. Tremblay, M. Boivin, R. DeV Peters, & R. G. Barr (Eds.), *Encyclopedia on early childhood development* [online] (pp. 1–8). Montreal, Canada: Centre of Excellence for Early Childhood Development. Retrieved from http://www.child-encyclopedia.com/sites/default/files/dossiers-complets/en/fetal-alcohol-spectrum-disorders-fasd.pdf

O'Connor, M. J., & Paley, B. (2009). Psychiatric conditions associated with prenatal alcohol exposure. *Developmental Disabilities Research Reviews, 15*(3), 225–234. http://doi.org/10.1002/ddrr.74

O'Connor, M. J., & Whaley, S. E. (2007). Brief intervention for alcohol use by pregnant women. *American Journal of Public Health, 97*(2), 252–258. http://doi.org/10.2105/AJPH.2005.077222

Office of the Surgeon General. (1981). Surgeon General's advisory on alcohol and pregnancy. *FDA Drug Bulletin, 11*(2), 9–10.

Office of the Surgeon General, US Department of Health and Human Services. (2005). *Advisory on alcohol use in pregnancy.* Washington, DC: Department of Health and Human Services. Retrieved from http://www.cdc.gov/ncbddd/fasd/documents/surgeongenbookmark.pdf

Olson, H. C., Ohlemiller, M. M., O'Connor, M. J., Brown, C. W., Morris, C. A., & Damus, K. (2009, March). *A call to action: Advancing essential services and research on fetal alcohol spectrum disorders – A report of the National Task Force on Fetal Alcohol Syn-*

drome and Fetal Alcohol Effect. Washington, DC: Superintendent of Documents, US Government Printing Office.

Olson, H. C., Oti, R., Gelo, J., & Beck, S. (2009). "Family matters": Fetal alcohol spectrum disorders and the family. *Developmental Disabilities Research Reviews, 15*(3), 235–249. http://doi.org/10.1002/ddrr.65

Paley, B., & O'Connor, M.J. (2011). Behavioral interventions for children and adolescents with fetal alcohol spectrum disorders. *Alcohol Research & Health, 34*(1), 64–75.

Perloff, R. M. (2008). *The dynamics of persuasion: Communication and attitudes in the 21st century* (3rd ed.). New York, NY: Erlbaum.

Pratt, R., Stephenson, J., & Mann, S. (2014). What influences contraceptive behaviour in women who experience unintended pregnancy? A systematic review of qualitative research. *Journal of Obstetrics and Gynaecology.* Advance online publication. http://doi.org/10.3109/01443615.2014.920783

Project CHOICES Intervention Research Group. (2003). Reducing the risk of alcohol-exposed pregnancies: A study of a motivational intervention in community settings. *Pediatrics, 111*(5), 1131–1135.

Project CHOICES Research Group. (2002). Alcohol-exposed pregnancy: Characteristics associated with risk. *American Journal of Preventive Medicine, 23*(3), 166–173. http://doi.org/10.1016/S0749-3797(02)00495-6

Rahman, M., Berenson, A. B., & Herrera, S. R. (2013). Perceived susceptibility to pregnancy and its association with safer sex, contraceptive adherence and subsequent pregnancy among adolescent and young adult women. *Contraception, 87*(4), 437–442. http://doi.org/10.1016/j.contraception.2012.09.009

Randall, C. L. (2001). Alcohol and pregnancy: Highlights from three decades of research. *Journal of Studies on Alcohol and Drugs, 62*(5), 554–561.

Reinert, D. F., & Allen, J. P. (2007). The alcohol use disorders identification test: An update of research findings. *Alcoholism, Clinical and Experimental Research, 31*(2), 185–199. http://doi.org/10.1111/j.1530-0277.2006.00295.x

Reynolds, K. D., Coombs, D. W., Lowe, J. B., Peterson, P. L., & Gayoso, E. (1995). Evaluation of a self-help program to reduce alcohol consumption among pregnant women. *The International Journal of the Addictions, 30* (4), 427–443. http://doi.org/10.3109/10826089509048735

Riley, E. P., Infante, M. A., & Warren, K. R. (2011). Fetal alcohol spectrum disorders: An overview. *Neuropsychology Review, 21*(2), 73–80. http://doi.org/10.1007/s11065-011-9166-x

Rollnick, S., Miller, W. R., & Butler, C. C. (2008). *Motivational interviewing in health care: Helping patients change behavior*. New York, NY: Guilford Press.

Royal College of Physicians of London. (1726). *Annals*. London, England: Author.

Roy, M., Dum, M., Sobell, L. C., Sobell, M. B., Simco, E. R., Manor, H., & Palmerio, R. (2008). Comparison of the quick drinking screen and the alcohol timeline followback with outpatient alcohol abusers. *Substance Use and Misuse, 43*(14), 2116–2123. http://doi.org/10.1080/10826080802347586

Saunders, J. B., Aasland, O. G., Babor, T. F., De La Fuente, J. R., & Grant, M. (1993). Development of the Alcohol Use Disorders Identification Test (AUDIT): WHO collaborative project on early detection of persons with harmful alcohol consumption – II. *Addiction, 88*, 791–804. http://doi.org/10.1111/j.1360-0443.1993.tb00822.x

Sayal, K., Heron, J., Golding, J., Alati, R., Smith, G. D., Gray, R., & Emond, A. (2009). Binge pattern of alcohol consumption during pregnancy and childhood mental health outcomes: Longitudinal population-based study. *Pediatrics, 123*(2), e289–e296. http://doi.org/10.1542/peds.2008-1861

Scott-Sheldon, L. A., Carey, K. B., Elliott, J. C., Garey, L., & Carey, M. P. (2014). Efficacy of alcohol interventions for first-year college students: A meta-analytic review of randomized controlled trials. *Journal of Consulting and Clinical Psychology, 82*(2), 177–188. http://doi.org/10.1037/a0035192

Smith, D.W. (1981). Fetal alcohol syndrome and fetal alcohol effects. *Neurobehavioral Toxicology and Teratology, 3*(2), 127.

Smith, P. C., Schmidt, S. M., Allensworth-Davies, D., & Saitz, R. (2009). Primary care validation of a single-question alcohol screening test. *Journal of General Internal Medicine, 24*(7), 783–788. http://doi.org/10.1007/s11606-009-0928-6

Sobell, L. C., Agrawal, S., Sobell, M. B., Leo, G. I., Young, L. J., Cunningham, J. A., & Simco, E. R. (2003). Comparison of a quick drinking screen with the timeline followback for individuals with alcohol problems. *Journal of Studies on Alcohol, 64*(6), 858–861.

Sobell, L. C., & Sobell, M. B. (1992). Timeline follow-back: A technique for assessing self-reported alcohol consumption. In J. Allen & R. L. Litten (Eds.), *Measuring alcohol consumption: Psychosocial and biological methods* (pp. 41–72). Totowa: NJ: Humana Press.

Sobell, L. C., & Sobell, M. B. (2011). *Group therapy with substance use disorders: A motivational cognitive-behavioral approach.* New York, NY: Guilford Press.

Sobell, L. C., Sobell, M. B., Johnson, K., Heinecke, N., & Agrawal, S. (2015). *Project Healthy CHOICES: A randomized controlled trial for preventing alcohol-exposed pregnancies using a brief postal intervention.* Manuscript submitted for publication.

Sobell, M. B., & Sobell, L. C. (1993). *Problem drinkers: Guided self-change treatment.* New York, NY: Guilford Press

Sobell, M. B., & Sobell, L. C. (2000). Stepped care as a heuristic approach to the treatment of alcohol problems. *Journal of Consulting and Clinical Psychology, 68*(4), 573–579. http://doi.org/10.1037/0022-006X.68.4.573

Sobell, M. B., Sobell, L. C., Johnson, K. E., & Bolton, B. G. (2007, July). *A media-based motivational intervention to reduce alcohol exposed pregnancies.* Paper presented at the Research Society on Alcoholism, Chicago, IL.

Stade, B., Ali, A., Bennett, D., Campbell, D., Johnston, M., Lens, C., & Koren, G. (2009). The burden of prenatal exposure to alcohol: Revised measurement of cost. *Canadian Journal of Clinical Pharmacology, 16*(1), e91–e102.

Stewart, S. H., Borg, K. T., & Miller, P. M. (2010). Prevalence of problem drinking and characteristics of a single-question screen. *The Journal of Emergency Medicine, 39*(3), 291–295. http://doi.org/10.1016/j.jemermed.2007.11.045

Stratton, K., Howe, C., & Battaglia, F. (1996). *Fetal alcohol syndrome: Diagnosis, epidemiology, prevention, and treatment.* Washington DC: National Academies.

Streissguth, A. P., Barr, H. M., Kogan, J., & Bookstein, F. L. (1996). *Understanding the occurrence of secondary disabilities in clients with fetal alcohol syndrome (FAS) and fetal alcohol effects (FAE): Final report to the Centers for Disease Control and Prevention (CDC).* (Technical Report No. 96-06). Seattle, WA: University of Washington, Fetal Alcohol & Drug Unit.

Streissguth, A. P., Bookstein, F. L., Barr, H. M., Sampson, P. D., O'Malley, K., & Young, J. K. (2004). Risk factors for adverse life outcomes in fetal alcohol syndrome and fetal alcohol effects. *Journal of Developmental & Behavioral Pediatrics, 25*(4), 228–238. http://doi.org/10.1097/00004703-200408000-00002

Substance Abuse and Mental Health Services Administration – SAMHSA. (2007). *Curriculum for addiction professionals (CAP): Level 1.* Retrieved from http://fasdcenter.samhsa.gov/educationTraining/courses/CapCurriculum/index.aspx

Substance Abuse and Mental Health Services Administration – SAMHSA. (2009). *Fetal alcohol spectrum disorders: The basics* [Powerpoint slides]. Retrieved http://www.fasdcenter.samhsa.gov/educationTraining/FASDBASICS/FASDTheBasics.pdf

Sullivan, W. C. (1899). A note on the influence of maternal inebriety on the offspring. *Journal of Mental Science, 45*, 489–503. http://doi.org/10.1192/bjp.45.190.489

Swanson, A. J., Pantalon, M. V., & Cohen, K. R. (1999). Motivational interviewing and treatment adherence among psychiatric and dually diagnosed patients. *Journal of Nervous and Mental Disease, 187*(10), 630–635. http://doi.org/10.1097/00005053-199910000-00007

Taj, N., Devera-Sales, A., & Vinson, D. C. (1998). Screening for problem drinking: Does a single question work? *The Journal of Family Practice, 46*(4), 328–335.

Thanh, N. X., & Jonsson, E. (2009). Costs of fetal alcohol spectrum disorder in Alberta, Canada. *Canadian Journal of Clinical Pharmacology, 16*(1), e80–90.

Trussell, J. (2011). Contraceptive failure in the United States. *Contraception, 83*(5), 397–404. http://doi.org/10.1016/j.contraception.2011.01.021

Tzilos, G. K., Sokol, R. J., & Ondersma, S. J. (2011). A randomized phase I trial of a brief computer-delivered intervention for alcohol use during pregnancy. *Journal of Women's Health, 20*(10), 1517–1524. http://doi.org/10.1089/jwh.2011.2732.

University of South Dakota, Sanford School of Medicine, Center for Disabilities. (2013). *Fetal alcohol spectrum disorders handbook.* Sioux Falls, SD: Author.

US Department of Agriculture. (2010). *Dietary guidelines for Americans, 2011* (7th ed.). Washington, DC: US Government Printing Office.

US Department of Health and Human Services. (2005). *Helping patients who drink too much: A clinician's guide.* (NIH Publication, no. 07-3769). Rockville, MD: National Institutes of Health, National Institute on Alcohol Abuse and Alcoholism. Retrieved from http://pubs.niaaa.nih.gov/publications/Practitioner/CliniciansGuide2005/clinicians_guide.htm

US Department of Health and Human Services. (2013). *Women's health USA,* 2012. Rockville, MD: Health Resources and Services Administration, Maternal and Child Health Bureau.

US Department of Health and Human Services, Office of Disease Prevention and Health Promotion. (2011). *Healthy People 2020.* Washington, DC: Author.

Velasquez, M. M., Ingersoll, K. S., Sobell, M. B., Floyd, R. L., Sobell, L. C., & von Sternberg, K. (2010). A dual-focus motivational intervention to reduce the risk of alcohol-exposed pregnancy. *Cognitive and Behavioral Practice, 17*(2), 203–212. http://doi.org/10.1016/j.cbpra.2009.02.004

Velasquez, M. M., von Sternberg, K., Kowalchuk, A., Parrish, D., Stephens, N., Seale, P., & Ostermeyer, B. (2014, June). *Preventing alcohol and tobacco-exposed pregnancies in primary care settings: Results of a randomized controlled trial.* Paper presented at the 37th annual meeting of the Research Society on Alcoholism, Bellevue, WA.

Velasquez, M. M., von Sternberg, K., & Parrish, D. E. (2013). CHOICES: An integrated behavioral intervention to prevent alcohol-exposed pregnancies among high-risk women in community settings. *Social Work in Public Health, 28*(3-4), 224–233. http://doi.org/10.1080/19371918.2013.759011

Warren, K. R., & Bast, R. J. (1988). Alcohol-related birth defects: An update. *Public Health Reports, 103*(6), 638–642.

Warren, K. R., Hewitt, B. G., & Thomas, J. D. (2010). Fetal alcohol spectrum disorders: Research challenges and opportunities. *Alcohol Research & Health: The Journal of the National Institute on Alcohol Abuse and Alcoholism, 34*(1), 4–14.

Wattendorf, D. J., & Muenke, M. (2005). Fetal alcohol spectrum disorders. *American Family Physician, 72*(2), 279–282.

Wedding, D., Kohout, J., Mengel, M. B., Ohlemiller, M., Ulione, M., Cook, K., . . . Braddock, S. (2007). Psychologists' knowledge and attitudes about Fetal Alcohol Syndrome, Fetal Alcohol Spectrum Disorders, and alcohol use during pregnancy. *Professional Psychology: Research and Practice, 38*(2), 208–213. http://doi.org/10.1037/0735-7028.38.2.208

Wilton, G., Moberg, D. P., Van Stelle, K. R., Dold, L. L., Obmascher, K., & Goodrich, J. (2013). A randomized trial comparing telephone versus in-person brief intervention to reduce the risk of an alcohol-exposed pregnancy. *Journal of Substance Abuse Treatment, 45,* 389–394. http://doi.org/10.1016/j.jsat.2013.06.006

Winograd, R. P., & Sher, K. J. (2015). *Binge drinking and alcohol misuse in young adults.* Cambridge, MA: Hogrefe. http://doi.org/10.1027/00403-000

World Health Organization. (2011). *The ICD-10 classification of mental and behavioural disorders: Clinical descriptions and diagnostic guidelines* (*Vol. 1*). Geneva, Switzerland: Author.

World Health Organization, Brief Intervention Study Group. (1996). A cross-national trial of brief interventions for heavy drinkers. *American Journal of Public Health, 86*(7), 948–955. Retrieved from http://ajph.aphapublications.org/

8

Appendix: Tools and Resources

This appendix includes tools and resources that practitioners can use to guide their work with women who are at risk of an AEP. These materials were used in the CHOICES study and have proven to be very useful resources clinically.

Appendix 1: Top Five Recommended FASD Resource Websites
These websites offer a plethora of resources for a variety of audiences on FASD prevention, diagnosis, and treatment.

Appendix 2: Links to Useful Clinical Guides, Brochures, and Resources for FASD Prevention
These links provide free resources and materials that can be used to guide practitioners as well as providing free materials for clients.

Appendix 3: Self-Evaluation Rulers for Alcohol and Birth Control
The self-evaluation rulers can be used to help clients assess their readiness to change their alcohol use and contraceptive behavior on a 10-point scale about the (a) importance of changing and (b) their confidence to achieve the change.

Appendix 4: Thinking About Drinking / Thinking About Birth Control
These decisional balance exercises can be used with women to raise awareness of their thoughts about alcohol and birth control behavior change.

Appendix 5: Brief Screening Tool for AEP Risk
This screening tool measures a woman's risk for an AEP and provides information about the correct use of multiple contraceptive methods.

Top Five Recommended FASD Resource Websites

Centers for Disease Control and Prevention (CDC)
http://www.cdc.gov/ncbddd/fasd/index.html
The US Centers for Disease Control and Prevention (CDC) is host to a variety of informative resources related to fetal alcohol spectrum disorders (FASDs). This includes basic fact sheets, scientific research and publications, and data and statistics. The CDC also provides free materials for practitioners, information regarding education and training, multimedia, and information for specific groups (e.g. health care providers, women, families, educators). Also note that the CHOICES intervention materials are available through this website.

National Organization on Fetal Alcohol Syndrome (NOFAS)
http://www.nofas.org
The National Organization on Fetal Alcohol Syndrome (NOFAS) aims to prevent alcohol-exposed pregnancies and support individuals, families, and communities living with FASD. NOFAS provides informational materials regarding FASD, prevention of FASD, and treatment of FASD. This website also offers resources and tools for various audiences.

Substance Abuse and Mental Health Services Administration (SAMHSA)
http://fasdcenter.samhsa.gov/index.aspx
Through their FASD Center for Excellence, SAMHSA provides an assortment of FASD resources in both English and Spanish. Relevant webinars, research, news, information regarding state systems, and screening and intervention programs can be accessed at this Web address. There are also "Grab and Go" dissemination materials that can be downloaded and printed for easy distribution in several different settings.

National Institute on Alcohol Abuse and Alcoholism (NIAAA)
http://www.niaaa.nih.gov/research/major-initiatives/fetal-alcohol-spectrum-disorders
FASD prevention is considered a major initiative of NIAAA. Their website provides an extensive collection of research materials, brochures, fact sheets, reports, clinical guides and manuals, other multimedia, and educational and classroom materials. There are also summaries of, and links to, FASD-related networks and consortiums for additional information and research-focused resources.

Collaborative Initiative on Fetal Alcohol Spectrum Disorders (CIFASD)
http://cifasd.org
The Collaborative Initiative on Fetal Alcohol Spectrum Disorders (CIFASD) is an interdisciplinary consortium sponsored by the National Institutes of Health that is focused on prevention of FASD, accurate diagnosis of FASD, and innovative interventions to treat those affected by FASD. Current research, publications, news, and multimedia educational materials are available through the consortium's website.

Links to Useful Clinical Guides, Brochures, and Resources for FASD Prevention

American College of Obstetricians and Gynecologists (ACOG) Drinking and Reproductive Health: Tool Kit for Clinicians: http://www.acog.org/About-ACOG/ACOG-Departments/Tobacco--Alcohol--and-Substance-Abuse/Drinking-and-Reproductive-Health-Tool-Kit-for-Clinicians

Centers for Disease Control and Prevention (CDC) CHOICES training materials, including *Counselor Manual, Client Workbook,* video demonstrations, and *Facilitator Guide*: http://www.cdc.gov/NCBDDD/fasd/freematerials.html

Centers for Disease Control and Prevention (CDC) handout on Project CHOICES, including answers to frequently asked questions (FAQ): http://www.cdc.gov/ncbddd/fasd/documents/choices_onepager_-april2013.pdf

Centers for Disease Control and Prevention (CDC) FASD Prevention free brochures, posters, fact sheets and training guides: http://www.cdc.gov/ncbddd/fasd/freematerials.html

National Institute on Alcohol Abuse and Alcoholism (NIAAA) Clinical guides and manuals: Resources for physicians, social workers, clinicians and other health care professionals": http://www.niaaa.nih.gov/publications/clinical-guides-and-manuals

National Organization on Fetal Alcohol Syndrome (NOFAS) Implementing CHOICES in clinical settings that serve American Indian and Alaska Native women of childbearing age: http://www.nofas.org/wp-content/uploads/2014/08/Implementing-CHOICES-in-Clinical-Settings-that-Serve-American-Indian-and-Alaska-Native-Women-of-Childbearing-Age.pdf

NOVA Southeastern University Guided Self Change website: Project Healthy CHOICES materials in English and Spanish: http://www.nova.edu/gsc/online_files.html

Self-Evaluation Ruler: Alcohol

On the line below, please circle the number that best reflects how **important** it is for you to drink below risky levels. (*Risky drinking* is defined as having 4 or more drinks per day or 8 or more drinks per week.)

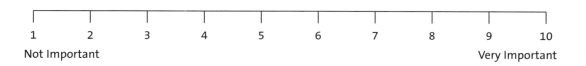

1	2	3	4	5	6	7	8	9	10

Not Important   Very Important

On the line below, please circle the number that best reflects how **confident** you are that you can drink below risky levels.

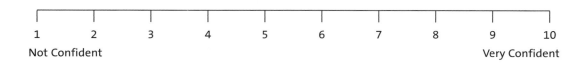

1	2	3	4	5	6	7	8	9	10

Not Confident   Very Confident

On the following scale, please circle the number that best reflects how **ready** you are at the present time to drink below risky levels?

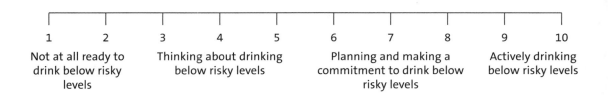

1	2	3	4	5	6	7	8	9	10
Not at all ready to drink below risky levels		Thinking about drinking below risky levels			Planning and making a commitment to drink below risky levels			Actively drinking below risky levels	

From: M. M. Velasquez, K. S. Ingersoll, M. B. Sobell, & L. C. Sobell:
Women and Drinking: Preventing Alcohol-Exposed Pregnancies

Self-Evaluation Ruler: Birth Control

On the line below, please circle the number that best reflects how **important** it is for you to use an effective birth control method every time you have sex.

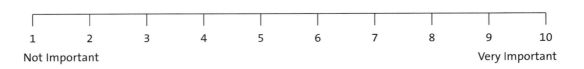

1	2	3	4	5	6	7	8	9	10
Not Important									Very Important

On the line below, please circle the number that best reflects how **confident** you are that you can use an effective birth control method every time you have sex.

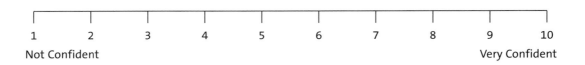

1	2	3	4	5	6	7	8	9	10
Not Confident									Very Confident

On the following scale, which number best reflects how **ready** you are at the present time to use birth control every time you have sex?

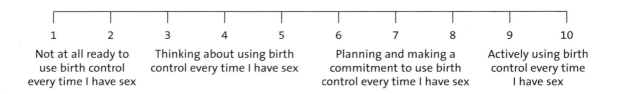

1	2	3	4	5	6	7	8	9	10
Not at all ready to use birth control every time I have sex		Thinking about using birth control every time I have sex			Planning and making a commitment to use birth control every time I have sex			Actively using birth control every time I have sex	

Thinking About Drinking

This will help you think about the **Good Things** and the **Not So Good Things** about your drinking. Weighing the **Good Things** and the **Not So Good Things** is what people do when they make decisions. For example, while drinking may sometimes help you relax, it could also cause you problems with your family or at work. Ask yourself, "what are the good things and not so good things about my current drinking?" and "what are the good things and not so good things about changing my drinking?"

Here's an example completed by another woman. Remember, every person has different reasons they might want to change their drinking.

Good things about my drinking:	Good things about changing my drinking:
More relaxed More comfortable with drinking friends Will not have to think about my problems for a while	More control over my life Support from family and friends Less legal trouble Better health

Not so good things about my drinking:	Not so good things about changing my drinking:
Disapproval from family and friends Costs too much money Increased chance of legal and job trouble	More stress or anxiety Feel more depressed Increased boredom

From: M. M. Velasquez, K. S. Ingersoll, M. B. Sobell, & L. C. Sobell:
Women and Drinking: Preventing Alcohol-Exposed Pregnancies   © 2016 Hogrefe Publishing

Use this page to complete your own thinking exercise about drinking. Remember, every woman is different, and your exercise will look different from the exercise on the previous page.

Good things about my drinking:	Good things about changing my drinking:

Not so good things about my drinking:	Not so good things about changing my drinking:

From: M. M. Velasquez, K. S. Ingersoll, M. B. Sobell, & L. C. Sobell:
Women and Drinking: Preventing Alcohol-Exposed Pregnancies

Thinking About Birth Control

This will help you think about the *Good Things* and the *Not So Good Things* about your use of birth control. Weighing the *Good Things* and the *Not So Good Things* is what people do when they make decisions. For example, while not using birth control may free you to have sex on the spur of the moment, it could also result in an unplanned pregnancy. Ask yourself, "what are the good things about my using birth control?" and "what are the not so good things about my using birth control every time I have sex?"

Good things about my using birth control:

I don't have to plan ahead for sex.
I won't get pregnant until I'm ready.
I will feel in control of my body.
I will respect myself.
When I am ready for a child, I will decide.
If I drink, I won't have to worry about harming my baby's health.

Not so good things about my using birth control:

I will have to plan ahead to protect myself.
I may have to discuss birth control with my partner, and that may be uncomfortable.
I will have to get a good birth control method.
Birth control could get expensive.

From: M. M. Velasquez, K. S. Ingersoll, M. B. Sobell, & L. C. Sobell:
Women and Drinking: Preventing Alcohol-Exposed Pregnancies   © 2016 Hogrefe Publishing

Use this page to complete your own thinking exercise about using birth control. Remember, every woman is different, and your exercise will look different from the exercise on the previous page.

Good things about my using birth control:

Not so good things about my using birth control:

Brief Screening Tool for AEP Risk

1. Have you ever had any of the following?

    Tubes Tied?   ☐ Yes   ☐ No

    Hysterectomy?   ☐ Yes   ☐ No

    Both ovaries removed?   ☐ Yes   ☐ No

2. How many times in the past year did you have 4 or more drinks in a day? *(One standard drink is equivalent to 12 ounces of beer, 5 ounces of wine, or 1.5 ounces of 80-proof spirits)*

    ☐ Never

    ☐ Less than monthly

    ☐ Monthly

    ☐ Weekly

    ☐ Daily or almost daily

3. Are you pregnant now?

    ☐ Yes   ☐ No

4. In the last 3 months have you had vaginal sex with a man?

    ☐ Yes   ☐ No

5. If you have had vaginal sex with a man in the past 3 months, **how often** did you use birth control?

Never	Rarely	Sometimes	Most of the Time	Almost Always	Always
☐	☐	☐	☐	☐	☐

6. Please place a check mark next to the type of birth control that you used in the past 3 months.

    ☐ Did not use birth control   ☐ Diaphragm/Cervical Cap

    ☐ Condoms   ☐ Vaginal ring (NuvaRing)

    ☐ Birth control pills   ☐ Morning After Pill

    ☐ Contraceptive patch   ☐ IUD

    ☐ Depo-provera injection   ☐ Sponge

    ☐ Implanon   ☐ Other

7. If you used birth control in the past 3 months please read the perfect use description for your type of birth control. Did you use the birth control in the past three months as described?

    ☐ Yes   ☐ No

From: M. M. Velasquez, K. S. Ingersoll, M. B. Sobell, & L. C. Sobell:
Women and Drinking: Preventing Alcohol-Exposed Pregnancies   © 2016 Hogrefe Publishing

Perfect Use Cards

Condoms (male and female)
- Must be used every time; must be used before expiration date; must not break during intercourse.
- Female condom must be inserted before penetration at the start of intercourse.
- Male condom must be in place before any genital contact and before penetration.

Emergency contraception (EC)
- Must only be used in emergency
- First pill recommended to be taken within 72 hours (3 days) of unprotected sex, but can be taken up to 120 hours (5 days); second pill must be taken 12 hours after first pill, or both pills can be taken at the same time.
- It is ineffective if used as the main form of contraception.

Birth control pills
- Must be taken on time every day, at the same time each day.
- Missing one pill but doubling up on the next day is still effective.
- It is ineffective until the following menstrual cycle if another, second pill is missed/doubled up on within the same pack.

Diaphragm/cervical cap
- Must be in place before intercourse.
- Spermicide must be spread around the cup.
- Must be kept in place 6 hours after intercourse.

NuvaRing
- Must be inserted for 3 whole weeks, and taken out for 1 week for bleeding.

Patch
- New patch must be put on an appropriate section of the body every week for 3 weeks, allowing one "patch-free" week for the menstrual cycle.

Depo-Provera shot
- Given every 11–13 weeks; schedule must be monitored by a doctor, use limited to 2 years.

Implanon
- Should have been inserted within the past 3 years.

Spermicide
- Must be inserted in the vagina at least 15 minutes before sex so it has time to dissolve and spread.
- Only effective for 1 hour and reapplication is needed before repeated sex.

Intrauterine device (IUD)
- A small T-shaped device with a copper wire, it is inserted into the uterus.
- Must be inserted and monitored by a health care provider.
- It is a good long-term, reliable method of contraception.
- Lasts up to 12 years.

From: M. M. Velasquez, K. S. Ingersoll, M. B. Sobell, & L. C. Sobell:
Women and Drinking: Preventing Alcohol-Exposed Pregnancies   © 2016 Hogrefe Publishing

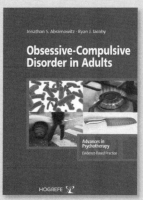

Advances in Psychotherapy
Evidence-Based Practice

View all
volumes at
www.hogrefe.com/
series/apt

Prices:
US $29.80 / £ 19.90 / € 24.95 per volume, standing order price US $24.80 / £ 15.90 / € 19.95 per volume (minimum 4 successive volumes) + postage & handling
Special rates for APA Division 12 and Division 42 Members

Order online at **www.hogrefe.com** or call toll-free **(800) 228-3749** (US only)

Hogrefe Publishing
30 Amberwood Parkway
Ashland, OH 44805, USA
Tel. +(800) 228-3749 / Fax: (419) 281-6883
E-Mail customerservice@hogrefe.com
www.hogrefe.com

Hogrefe Publishing
Merkelstraße 3
37085 Göttingen, Germany
Tel. +49 551 9 99 50-0 / Fax -111
E-Mail customerservice@hogrefe.com
www.hogrefe.com

Advances in Psychotherapy
Evidence-Based Practice

"The authors have assembled a helpful resource for clinicians in counseling or health centers, filling a gap in the clinical literature. The clinical tips for optimizing clinical interactions with college drinkers and the guidelines for assessment and treatment planning will be particularly useful to college health professionals."

Kate Carey, PhD, Professor, Department of Behavioral and Social Sciences and Center for Alcohol and Addiction Studies, Brown University School of Public Health, Providence, RI

Rachel P. Winograd, Kenneth J. Sher

Binge Drinking and Alcohol Misuse Among College Students and Young Adults

Volume 32
2015, vi + 92 pp.
ISBN 978-0-88937-403-4
US $29.80 / £ 19.90 / € 24.95

Heavy drinking – and its associated problems – are an integral part of many college students' and other young adults' lives. Though some young drinkers are able to consume alcohol without incident, many face significant negative fallout from their excessive consumption. This volume describes the nature of alcohol misuse, its epidemiology, its causes, and methods for treatment, specifically as they pertain to college students and other young adults. It provides practitioners and trainees with a range of evidence-based treatment approaches to help clients change their alcohol use habits. The information presented is both thorough and concise and will help readers with varied backgrounds and experience improve their understanding of the many nuanced factors involved in assessing and treating problematic drinking in young adults.

Stephen A. Maisto, Gerard J. Connors, Ronda L. Dearing

Alcohol Use Disorders

Volume 10
2007, viii + 94 pp.
ISBN 978-0-88937-317-4
US $29.80 / £ 19.90 / € 24.95

Practice-oriented, evidence-based guidance on treating alcohol problems – one of the most widespread health problems in modern society.

Hogrefe Publishing
30 Amberwood Parkway
Ashland, OH 44805, USA
Tel. +(800) 228-3749 / Fax: (419) 281-6883
E-Mail customerservice@hogrefe.com
www.hogrefe.com

Hogrefe Publishing
Merkelstraße 3
37085 Göttingen, Germany
Tel. +49 551 9 99 50-0 / Fax -111
E-Mail customerservice@hogrefe.com
www.hogrefe.com